15

Living with
Leopards

Nils Kure

SUNBIRD
PUBLISHING

First published 2003
2 4 6 8 10 9 7 5 3 1
Sunbird Publishing (Pty) Ltd, 34 Sunset Avenue, Llandudno, Cape Town, South Africa
Registration number: 4850177827

Copyright © 2003 published edition: Sunbird Publishing
Copyright © 2003 text: Nils Kure
Copyright © 2003 photographs: Nils Kure

Publisher Dick Wilkins
Editor Maysun Najjar
Design concept Terry Norridge Austen
DTP layout Mandy McKay
Production Manager Andrew de Kock

Reproduction by Unifoto (Pty) Ltd, Cape Town
Printed and bound by Tien Wah Press (Pte) Ltd, Singapore

ISBN 1-91993-809-5

Contents

Acknowledgements

Thanks are primarily owing to Mala Mala's owner, Mr. Michael Rattray, for building the reserve into its current size, without which a study of this nature would not have been possible.

The term "visionary" is much in vogue today, often used to obscure an evident lack of logic or planning. It was not as well used thirty years ago, when the process of acquiring the properties in the Sabi Sand that bordered the Kruger National Park on the east and had the only river in the area running through them began, but the result is a clear example of solid forethought, the advantages of which are obvious to the rangers who have worked in it and the guests that they have guided.

I am also most grateful to have been given a completely free hand in writing this book and bringing it to press.

My father, Arne Kure, converted the outdated program that was used to write the book into forms suitable for productions of first drafts and mailing to the publisher.

Mike Lawes at the University of Natal and Ant Maddock from the Natal Parks Board were very helpful in sourcing reference material.

I took out a number of photographers over the years, and benefited from their advice. In particular I would like to recognise Gerald Hinde, Horst Klem and Andrej Sawaj, who were unstinting in sharing their knowledge.

Tony Girling, Rob Wynne, Jeff Wardropper and Mike Loveridge from Photoworld, and Dennis da Silva at Beith Laboratories processed my film to exacting standards and provided specialised assistance in unconventional situations.

Kim Wolhuter and Dale Hancock were based at Mala Mala while producing the documentary Beauty and the Beasts and the subsequent book 'A Time with Leopards'. It was a pleasure to work with them and we shared data and photographs to our mutual benefit.

The association with the publishing team has been a very happy one. Abed Najjar of Sahara Press took the project on with great and unflagging enthusiasm, Maysun Najjar edited a large and involuted text into manageable proportions, and Terry Norridge Austen laid out the text and pictures. I am very appreciative of the hospitality that I received from Matt and Terry Austen and Bruce and Barbara Norridge during two visits to England for the final editing. And thanks are also due to the team at Sunbird Publishing for tying up all the loose ends and bringing the book to fruition.

Ultimately the dedication of this book should be to the guests that I guided while working as a ranger. With them I have a long and ongoing association, many shared memories and some lasting friendships.

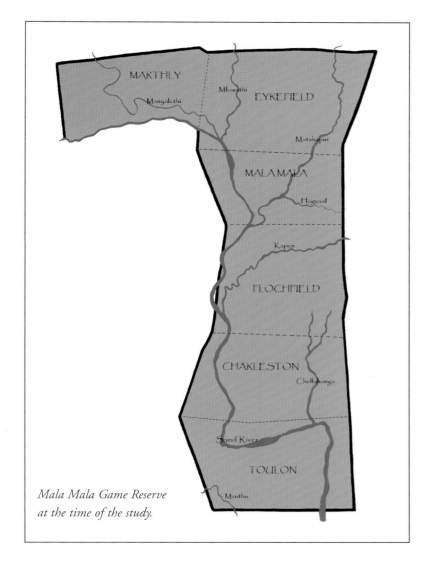

Mala Mala Game Reserve at the time of the study.

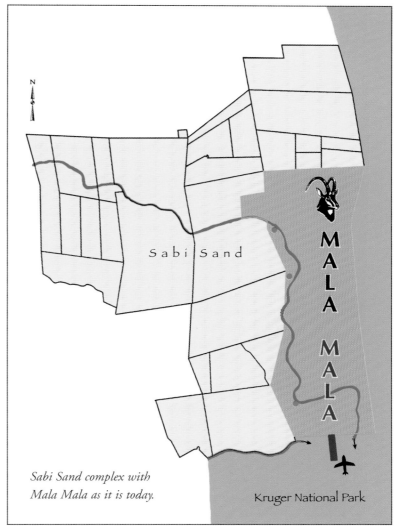

Sabi Sand complex with Mala Mala as it is today.

Introduction

This book is an abridgement of a study based on eight years of data collected on leopards at Mala Mala Game Reserve. The original form is far too lengthy for publication in this format, which necessitated the removal of many maps and all the tabular data, along with their analyses. Much of its content has thereby assumed an apparently authoritarian nature, with bald statements and sweeping generalisations. It must be borne in mind that these are conclusions based on often intermittent observations, that some of the assessments are subjective, and anything that is presented seemingly as fact is subject to revision.

The words of Avi the Learned, an Icelandic historian, writing in the 12th century, have eternal relevance in this regard: "*But if anything is mistaken in this book, one should prefer whatsoever proves to be more accurate.*"

The result is a text that is partly statement of fact and partly anecdotal. Individual animals have been referred to by name throughout the text without introduction or supporting descriptions; I have, however, retained these references since many who read this book will recognise them. Almost without exception, the photographs and observations were taken and made whilst guiding guests in the reserve. Reference is made in the text to a documentary on leopards filmed on Mala Mala by Kim Wolhuter and Dale Hancock and produced by Richard Goss, entitled Beauty and the Beasts. The adult leopards in the film were the Chellahanga female and the Jakkalsdraai male. There was a good deal of mutually beneficial exchange of information between ourselves and the film crew and mention is made of them several times in the text; for convenience, I have referred to them simply as Kim and Dale.

Besides the data that was obliged to be omitted from this publication, there is a wealth of new information that has come to light from our ongoing system of records. It is intended that both be brought to print in the fullness of time. Beyond these considerations, this is in essence an account of an intimate and personal association with Africa's most striking and secretive large predator. I hope that I have conveyed some of the fascination that I have for these animals, and that you enjoy reading about the leopards I knew as much as I enjoyed writing about them.

Observation and Familiarization

Most of the observations that follow in this book were made on animals that were habituated to the presence of vehicles; that paid us no heed whatsoever, and could be followed, sometimes for hours at a stretch, while they went about their business quite unaffected by our presence. This state of affairs is uncommon in leopards compared with the other large cats in Africa, the lion and the cheetah, and has resulted in them attaining an almost legendary aura of mystery. Of all the common large animals in Africa, the one that is typically the most difficult to find is the leopard.

RIGHT Alert and calculating, even in repose.

CHAPTER ONE

ABOVE The Mlowathi male making use of a bush track at the start of an evening patrol.

Throughout South Africa, leopards can still be found on farmland, where they have always been, co-existing with their human neighbours to greater and lesser degrees, depending on the attitudes and behaviour of both parties. Reserves that are too small to contain lions or cheetahs show signs that they are occupied by leopards, but the animals themselves are seldom if ever seen. Their best defence against humans lies in secrecy, and they do it very well.

A lion or a cheetah which is indifferent to vehicles is a common sight in Africa. A leopard is not, or used not to be. Like their relatives, leopards are also capable of realising that vehicles represent, in areas where animals are only viewed, no danger to them. It just takes a lot longer for this to happen, and usually a fair amount of work in the sense of consistent and considerate behaviour on the part of whoever is driving the vehicle.

Habituated leopards are not especially common, yet nor are they as unique and as entirely a latter-day phenomenon as might sometimes be supposed. George Schaller, in his classic study on lions (1966-69) in Serengeti National Park, included observations made on the leopards in the Seronera area, which he described as being "... quite indifferent to

vehicles". Jonathan Scott photographed an habituated female and her cubs in the Masai Mara National Reserve, which is generally unsuited to leopards as a whole.

They have been seen over the years, usually infrequently, in most large National Parks. Turnbull-Kemp and Wilson detailed numerous observations in Zimbabwe on leopards that had to varying degrees become habituated to people. In the Cape Province, the "friendly leopard", that was seen and even photographed by several groups of hikers became quite famous for a while.

The best likelihood of animals becoming habituated and well-known is usually to be found in private reserves, or in the areas where private operators work concessions on State land or in National Parks.

In these areas vehicles are out on a daily basis looking for game, which gives animals a good deal of exposure to them. Eventually, individuals from even the shier species will start to accept their presence. It is then essential, once an animal is seen, that its experience of vehicles does not entirely put it off them in the future.

An animal that is vigorously pursued in an effort to get a better look at it may think twice about letting itself be seen again. Sometimes,

ABOVE This was the first time the Hogvaal female was seen suckling her cubs.

an animal that moves off and is cautiously followed will settle down and allow itself to be viewed at a distance; others may simply try to remain unseen. At that point it should be left and over the months and years, if treated in this manner, it may permit the distance that it is comfortable with to grow shorter and shorter.

As a very general rule of thumb, I would say that it can take approximately two years for a nervous animal to become accustomed to vehicles. It is difficult to be at all precise about this figure since nervous animals that try to avoid vehicles are not easy to positively identify, so that one cannot be certain when an animal that has relaxed down in such a fashion was first seen.

This appears to have been the time that it took for the Hogvaal female to have become accustomed to us. The time will also vary according to individual character; some leopards are far bolder or more tranquil, if such a term can be applied to them, than others, which may never become habituated. We used to call an unhabituated animal a nervous one, while one that had become used to vehicles was known as a relaxed individual. I have used these same terms throughout the rest of the book.

The process of habituating a population of leopards starts to snowball once females start relaxing, since their subsequent litters then grow up with vehicles and become, potentially, the most indifferent of all – provided they are properly handled at all times.

Once an animal has relaxed down, it is important that it continues to receive exactly the same careful handling. Vehicles must behave in a consistent fashion; they then become predictable to an animal. I found it surprising how completely an initially nervous animal might eventually accept us. The Hogvaal female was an animal who, I believe, we saw over about two years before she relaxed down. The duration is difficult to assess since she never gave us enough of a view to be certain that it was the same animal, but over this period a small adult female with the same habits was seen in much the same area. When found – invariably by a sharp-eyed tracker, while she was flattening herself to the ground – she would lie still until certain she had been seen, whereupon she rushed out at the vehicle in a short dash of a few paces. Then she stood, ears back and tail flicking, for a few moments before turning and walking off. After about ten paces the walk broke into a trot and she would find a bush to hide in.

ABOVE A young male leopard is curious but unconcerned about the vehicle in his path.

When she was found again, the process would be repeated. It appeared that we were dealing with an animal that knew her mind, and one with a fair amount of self-possession to boot. She was not nervous of the vehicles so much as she disliked having them around, it seemed; for after having demonstrated, she did not run off but stood a while, in evident irritation, before trying to lose them again. We were careful not to stay with her too long, so we viewed her, and left.

One morning, a leopard whose behaviour answered very much to this general description was found several hundred metres from the Matshapiri river. The terrain was covered in knee-high grass and encroached with low, leafy kiaat bushes, which well suited her evasive tactics. But after she had hidden from us two or three times, she seemed to come to some sort of decision, and walked down the slope toward the river, ignoring us completely.

We followed, as she picked her way down the crumbling banks of the river and walked upstream in the sand, turning where the Hogvaal donga fed into the larger system. She walked several hundred metres up this tributary to a large, slightly rounded slab of granite that protruded from the bank into the sand. Here she lay down and started calling; within a minute, two tiny cubs crept from within a crevice and she suckled them, with no further regard for us.

What do animals think of us, under these conditions? I would give a great deal to know. A vehicle is very new to Africa, unlike the human shape which is well known and over millennia of domination has

This is how game viewing in an open vehicle is usually explained, and on the surface it seems to work. If one stands up in a vehicle that is close to predators, the results are usually instantaneous and they react with fear or aggression.

This is not, however, the whole of the story. Lions and leopards do seem to know that there are people in the cars; they just accept that, so long as they are seated, there is nothing to fear from them. If someone is moving around, or doing something that attracts their attention, they look that person directly in the eye. There can be little doubt in my mind that they know exactly what it is that they are dealing with. These perceptions can be tested by slowly standing up; as one rises higher, the predator becomes more watchful and then will start to show signs of flight or of aggression. Sit down, and it relaxes again.

If the first explanation held true, that an animal does not identify a seated person in a vehicle as a human, then it should react as soon as that identity becomes apparent and run from the vehicle with its suddenly evident occupants, or charge at it, as it would treat a person on foot. But this does not happen. Why it should be that these animals evidently recognise us for what we are, yet ignore us sometimes completely so long as our posture is not threatening, I do not know.

It became apparent to me that looking them directly in the eye has little effect. This hostile (to primates, anyway) act is generally perceived as a grave error when dealing with animals. Like getting between a hippo and the water, it is sometimes regarded as one of the basic mistakes that can be made in the bush. However I have tested its application and found the theory, so far, to be lacking in substance. One can stare, glare or frown directly into the eyes of a lion or leopard with no evident results. Perhaps it has to do with the remarkable disinterest that they have for someone sitting in a vehicle. The situation might be quite different were one to meet the same animal on the ground. I cannot vouch for this situation, and it would be foolish to put it to the test.

How does one treat an animal with consideration? In essence this involves not doing what it evidently does not like. Different individuals may require different treatment, but a few basic generalities hold true for almost all of them. Driving directly at an animal tends to make it edgy, even at a distance far beyond that at which it may tolerate a vehicle. The best method of approach is to drive in an oblique fashion, aiming at a point to its side, and thereby draw closer. Engaging in low ratio is a good idea, since this not only results in the vehicle moving slowly but keeps the engine beat at a steady rate. Moving only one vehicle at a time and limiting the number at a sighting were also practices that we followed stringently, and it is vital, in my mind, that all the vehicles are driven with identical regard for these rules.

Consistency is a very important thing; no-one likes dealing with a person who is erratic in behaviour and animals should be no different. If they know exactly what to expect from any vehicle, they will be at ease in its presence. If, however, they cannot be certain how someone is going to approach and behave around them, they will view all of them with justifiable suspicion.

Some animals seem to have better and worse days much as we do. Leopards have very expressive features and postures, which become obvious to anyone who has spent any time with them, and quickly indicate that on certain days it may be necessary to view a particular individual from a longer distance, or with fewer vehicles. Females with

engendered amongst animals an instinctive respect born of fear. Vehicles, however, elicit no preconceived responses. Large as they are, they are deserving of caution and an animal seeing one for the first time may put a good deal of distance between itself and this unknown monster. Treated carefully, however, they soon assume that it is no threat to them and accept its presence.

The simple explanation for this is easily assumed; as a human, walking around, one is easily recognised and identified. When sitting in a vehicle, however, the animal perceives the people within as part of a whole. So long as a person does not stand up or get out of a vehicle, by either action identifying himself as a feared enemy, an habituated animal will accept him as part of the larger, strange new creature.

small cubs can be aggressive and may need to be given a wide berth. Apart from the considerations accorded to the mother, it is essential that the cub is given very particular treatment during its earlier months. Once it has left its den, we view it initially with only one vehicle, later introducing others to a maximum of three. In this way vehicles become a natural part of its environment.

Night time is especially good for watching leopards and lions. They undergo what amounts to almost a personality change, becoming far more confident. The hours of darkness belong to them and their superior vision in poor light ensures this. Humans, predators and persecutors of their competitors by day, were until the development of such technologies as artificial light and projectile weapons entirely powerless at night. The transfer of advantage that happens with the changing of day into night is almost absolute and is perhaps most clearly exemplified in the case of the Man-Eating Leopard of Rudraprayag, which for eight long years lived off the people of the Garwhal district in northern India. During the day, people conducted their affairs under no constraints, while the leopard lay up somewhere and avoided contact with them. As the sun was going down, the population hurried to places of shelter, quickly ate the evening meal and, once the darkness was complete, settled into a deathly silence for fear of attracting the man-eater's attentions to them.

During these hours, the leopard prowled at will among the villages, sometimes boldly and noisily trying to break into one of the dwellings. This is an extreme and rather exotic state of affairs, for leopards very seldom take to feeding on humans. It does, however, show very markedly how their attitude differs at night, and this is evident in game-viewing situations. An animal that is nervous during the day and runs from vehicles may be almost completely indifferent at night, and permit itself to be followed and watched by several vehicles. This is quite likely one of the reasons why they have become thought of as nocturnal animals, an issue more fully discussed later on.

So much for the mechanics and theories of habituating animals. With leopards this does not happen overnight. Mala Mala began operating as a game-viewing concern in 1965. For the next fifteen odd years, leopards were a very infrequent sighting but the situation improved very gradually as specific individuals became used to vehicles.

When I arrived in 1988, the leopard viewing was good, and for this we relied on about five individual animals. Over the years the number grew, so that by 1993 we had identified about twenty-five individuals, including subadults, that were habituated to varying degrees. This figure seems to have remained more or less constant ever since.

Leopards are being seen more frequently now than was ever the case before, simply because of this process. In the Kruger National Park and in Hluhluwe, they are not uncommonly seen, and visitors to the Luangwe Valley in Zambia stand a good chance of seeing one over the course of a few days. The southern part of the KNP (Kruger National Park), including the Sabi Sand, probably supports as concentrated a population of leopards as can be expected to occur anywhere, owing to the dense vegetation and above all the abundance of suitable prey, particularly impalas. Within this very favourable terrain, the number of

RIGHT Of all the many moods that are reflected on their expressive faces, my favourite is the whimsical.

THIS PAGE White-faced owls feed on a variety of small prey; this one comes to terms with an unusually large and spiny grasshopper.

leopards that may be viewed is dependent firstly on the number of habituated animals within one's area, which in turn depends on the size of the land at one's disposal. For these reasons I believe it is accurate to say that Mala Mala has the largest number of habituated leopards within its boundaries than any other reserve. Apart from the wonderful consistency and diversity of viewing that this provided, with leopards being seen on a regular basis and the sightings comprising individuals of differing ages and sexes, the basis was formed for a significant study to be made.

With continuity of observation, individuals and lineages can be followed over time. The territorial relationships between animals of the same sex, and the associations between the sexes are recorded. Above all, because of the size of the land available to us, when subadults matured and struck out on their own, we did not necessarily lose contact with them through their moving across our borders. This is particularly significant in males, who occupy larger ranges and may move further afield from their natal area than do females.

Thus we were able to follow the careers of two dominant males that we had known from the time they were cubs, as well as one whom we first saw as a young adult. For a time, a golden period of a few years, these three animals were territorial over almost all of the land that we covered, and interacted and mated with a large number of females, some of whose mothers and grandmothers were known to us. The situation provided opportunities for many unique observations.

ABOVE *The large-spotted genet is very much at ease in trees and its varied diet includes bird nestlings.*

ABOVE *The African wild cat was domesticated in Egypt to become the ancestor of domestic stock.*
OVERLEAF *Summer rains in Buffalo Pans create a pan for the Hogvaal female from which to drink.*

The
Elusive Cat

From the crispness of its outlines in the sharply angled morning light, and the fact that it lies over the tracks left by an early rising francolin and not under them, we conclude that the leopard who left his spoor on the road we are travelling passed this way within the previous hour. The breadth of the pad, larger than that of any female yet smaller than the prints of an adult male, identify the owner as a young male, and since we know of such an animal in this area who is accustomed to us and will permit himself to be viewed, the trail is deemed worthy of following.

RIGHT *Sometimes a leopard's eyes are the only clue to its presence.*

CHAPTER TWO

ABOVE *Spoor of a young male leopard.*

ABOVE *Vervet monkeys have acute eyesight and are reliable witnesses to the presence of predators.*

ABOVE *Elephants dig for water in the dry bed of the Matshapiri river.*

It heads directly along the road, through the patch of fine sand that it was first detected crossing, and disappears as it moves onto harder ground. Driving ahead, we find the spoor again where it has once more entered into more favourable terrain, and proceed in this fashion for a hundred metres or so, losing it and relocating it further ahead. Finally it disappears and does not re-emerge, although the road ahead is covered with a good layer of sand well suited to our purposes.

Dismounting, we follow it carefully from the point where it last left the sand and find where it moved off the road and into the adjacent grassland. The grass has started to die with the onset of winter but is still thick enough that picking out the trail will be painstaking and time-consuming. It is heading toward the Matshapiri river, which is a logical destination for a leopard, and so, leaving a branch in the road in case we are not successful in cutting ahead and later have need of taking up the trail again at this place, we make for an entry point down the steep bank and into the dry river course with the hope of cutting the spoor in its sandy bed.

Our luck is in; almost exactly opposite to where the spoor was left on the road, we find it moving down the bank and entering the river bed, where it heads upstream. Following the line of craters left by our quarry's paws is an easy matter as long as they remain in the sand and progress is rapid for a few hundred metres. Suddenly the tracker snaps his fingers and the engine is instantly killed.

Ahead of us, where he is pointing, a monkey can now be heard raising the alarm. It is more than likely that it is shouting at the leopard whose tracks we are following, and as we can return to the spoor at leisure and it is needful to find the monkey before it loses sight of the predator, we abandon the trail and waste no time in the pursuit.

Our furry informer is still vocalising when we arrive at his station, staring at a point which appears to be some distance beyond the western bank. A short period of time lapses before we find a route up it, and when we reach the approximate area there is nothing in sight and the monkey has fallen silent.

Casting about, however, the tracks of a young male leopard come to light in a bare patch of ground. His lead, which was estimated at about an hour when we began tracking, has been cut to less than five minutes. From this point on, however, things take a turn for the worse. The trail is indistinct in the dense bush and one does not wish to spend too much time walking on it for fear the animal sees us on foot and takes fright, increasing his lead and maybe spooking him to the extent that he is reluctant to permit even the vehicle within viewing range. Driving ahead in the direction the spoor was taking yields nothing, and eventually we are forced to return and try to untangle the tracks. They are found to have doubled back within thirty metres of our last clear sighting and moved north along the river bank.

Driving in the same direction in the river bed is unproductive, and checking the western bank further ahead shows that the leopard has headed west, away from the river and into fairly densely wooded savannah terrain. An hour later, we are no closer to our goal and the pursuit is abandoned. Leopards are much inclined to travel in a circuitous fashion with a good deal of doubling back, and perhaps this tendency has kept him just beyond our reach.

However, his route shows a pattern more of deliberate avoidance than of coincidental divergence, and it is likely that we have been

ABOVE The dense vegetation along river banks is favoured by bushbuck and duikers, and hence by the leopards that prey upon them.

following a shy individual, wary of vehicles and unwilling to be found. Contrary to what is often taken to be the case, a leopard is not most likely to be found up a tree. Nor, in the area that I had experience of them, did one stand anything but the remotest of likelihoods of finding one in the rocky outcrops and koppies. Probably the majority of photographs published of leopards show them in trees, and perhaps tend to fix an image in the mind of a leopard as an arboreal animal. However, this is probably because a photograph of a leopard in a tree is usually more spectacular than one taken of the animal on the ground. Moreover, the latter picture is often difficult to take at all owing to the tendency of the animal to be obscured by vegetation.

For these reasons, by far the greater number of my own photographs are of leopards in trees, yet I can recall very few occasions that I actually found one aloft. Consequently, people in the guiding business are sometimes heard to say that leopards are hardly ever to be found in trees. The truth lies in between. Although they are not as arboreal as pictures in circulation might suggest, they do spend a

significant amount of their time in trees. And though I very seldom found one aloft, I did spend a lot of time watching leopards in trees. They had either climbed up while we were following them or were lazing around the site of a kill. If a comfortable branch is to be found in the vicinity, a leopard may spend a fair amount, though not necessarily the major portion, of its time lying in a tree rather than on the ground. In an area where the animals are not habituated to vehicles, however, the best chance of seeing a leopard perhaps is up a tree.

In such an area, the probability of coming close enough to an animal on the ground that it might be seen, is small, and it is most likely to be spotted at a distance which it is comfortable with and feels no urge to flee. In the type of vegetation that they show preference for throughout their range, namely the thicker variety, the only place where it is likely to be seen at all under such conditions is in a tree, or on an elevated rock.

Twelve koppies, ranging in height from approximately seven metres to perhaps thirty, are sprinkled around the reserve. Their boulder-strewn

ABOVE Chestnutbacked finchlark chicks.

slopes, bound with vegetation, look tailor-made for leopards but are in general devoid of the large cats. They are certainly in demand as den sites for small cubs. In this respect there probably exists no finer place. Adults were, however, hardly ever seen on them and with a little reflection it becomes clear that no reason exists for them to be there. Away from the protection of a reserve, a refuge may be important and it is easy to see a leopard electing to lie up during the day in a high, rocky, overgrown place.

In a protected area where no such prudence is required, a predator is likely to be found in the places favoured by its prey, in conditions best suited to its capture. For the leopard, the scrubby ecotone savannah with its herds of impalas and the reed-beds and riverine vegetation where the solitary bushbuck and duiker lurk, are the most suitable habitats. Although the koppies are presumably favourable to the stalk and pounce hunting methods employed by leopards, the only prey to be found on them is the nimble klipspringer, better suited to escape in its chosen habitat than is any predator to its capture. These then were the areas where one was most likely to encounter leopards. The dense woodlands and savannahs and the overgrown banks and beds of the rivers and erosion courses. Perhaps the most significant factor, however, that determines the most suitable places where leopards might be found and viewed is the accessibility of the area to vehicles.

The southern part of the reserve may have been the best of all from a leopard's point of view. Overgrown and dissected by ravines, it supported a population that was probably as high as was to be found anywhere else in the reserve and maybe higher. These features, however, made it, in many places, difficult if not impossible to traverse. With fewer roads and poorer visibility, it also meant that finding the animals in the first place was not as easy, let alone following them thereafter. More than the right habitat in which leopards might be found, however, it was the specific areas that we looked in for particular individuals that provided most of our viewing.

For most of the time that I spent in the reserve, the number of relaxed animals available to us for viewing averaged around twenty-five. It was a strange and fairly constant feature that, at any time, we were reliant on just a few or even only one of these individuals for our

ABOVE Klipspringers mark their territory using secretions from a pre-orbital gland.

viewing. A few, like the Hogvaal female, had ranges that were partly off our property. She might therefore disappear into that part of her range for months at a time.

Other animals, whose ranges were mainly on our land, would simply go through periods when they were easily and regularly found, followed by times when they seemed to disappear entirely. It became evident that leopards do concentrate on a particular part of their range for a certain period of time, and when this happened to be in an area where they were easily located we probably saw more of them. The most convenient viewing that I remember came about with females and their cubs.

When the cubs are small – up to perhaps a month and a half or two of age – they are kept in a den, the position of which is changed every few days or weeks so that the smell which it acquires over time does not attract the attention of other predators. During this time, if a den can be found and relocated after the periodic moves, viewing is virtually guaranteed. In two instances, with the Mlowathi male and again with the Trollip's Crossing female's last two cubs, a time existed just before the cubs were abandoned by their mothers, at the age of about twenty months, when we hardly required to look for them at all. The cubs were found virtually every day, and sometimes twice in a day, during both the morning and afternoon drives, lying on or close to the

road. The mother periodically appeared in order to lead her offspring to a kill she had made, and during the time that this state of affairs lasted, they all remained within a small area. This happened in the summer of 1990 in the case of the Mlowathi male, and the autumn of 1995 with the Trollip's Crossing cubs.

So regularly were the latter seen, in fact, that the rangers working from Harry's camp, on which doorstep the young leopards were effectively camping, complained to those of us further north how they had to carefully plan their routes out of camp in order to avoid bumping into the leopards – again – thereby wasting valuable time that they desired to spend in looking for other animals. It was gratuitous one-upmanship, of course, but while that period lasted there was probably, on occasion, a grain of truth in what they said.

Male leopards conduct regular patrols of their territories and can fall into habitual patterns that last for a span of time. During one winter, every few days either the Flockfield male or the Jakkalsdraai male would walk north up the eastern bank of the Sand river, marking at specific localities. The next day, whoever had made the patrol was invariably followed by the other, marking over the scents left by his rival. Both leopards used to leave the river at much the same place and move east, eventually crossing into the Kruger National Park. It was an easy matter, during that period, to cut ahead along their known route and locate

ABOVE The densely vegetated slopes of Sithlawayise, one of several granite koppies in the area. Most of the koppies in this area are equally well covered with bush and serve as ideal den sites for lions as well as leopards.

them if their spoor had been found, or if they had been lost in the reeds while we were following them. These easier periods were interleaved with more arid patches, when leopards appeared thin on the ground and were not easily come by. Apart from the natural factors that affected our finding them, luck was also involved. One might for instance on a particular day hear a kudu raising the alarm, follow up on it and find the spoor of a leopard heading through the bush, track the animal up hill and down dale and finally notice a giraffe looking with meaning at something which turns out, on investigation, to be the leopard. This is a gratifying state of affairs in which various forms of bushcraft can be used to impressive effect, but only because events have conspired to make them available.

On the other hand, there is the frustration of driving along and finding nothing, neither spoor nor call, to begin with. There is also the good and the bad of kills. If a leopard is found on a kill, then viewing is virtually guaranteed for as long as the food lasts. However, if the kill has been made where it can not be seen from the road and the leopard left no tracks in the process, it is unlikely to be discovered. The West Street female had a smaller appetite than other leopards and once spent five days with the carcass of a female bushbuck. She therefore gave us a good deal of viewing but conversely was out of circulation for similar lengths of time on the occasions that she was not found while lying up with a kill.

On the 23rd of February 1991, the Matshapiri female was found in a tree on the edge of a waterhole, with the carcass of a waterbuck calf. This was during the course of the morning drive. After lunch, my friend William Taylor and I went for a run and encountered a large drag mark crossing the main road. Looking in the direction it was taking, the carcass of an adult female impala could be seen lying at the base of a tree growing out of a termite mound. That afternoon it was investigated during the drive and found to have been the handiwork of the Sparta female, who had her young male offspring in attendance. Five hundred metres down the same road, the Airstrip female was shortly thereafter discovered in the branches of a scented thorn with the carcass of a duiker. In the south, the Flockfield male was found near Rocky Crossing. He was sleeping in the shade of a tree wherein was stored his kill, an aardvark. And that evening, on the other side of the river to the north, a male leopard which had recently killed an impala and dragged it into the grass, was found. Those five kills were the highest number that have yet been found in a single day. Apart from a little skill involved in locating some of them, the event was mainly owing to circumstance in that they had been made so close to the roads, and that the roads in question were travelled that day.

The seasons have a great effect on the likelihood of finding leopards. The worst time is during the first part of summer, from December to February. Following an average rainfall, the vegetation is at this time exceedingly lush and the grass, in most places, as high as or slightly higher than a leopard. A supine animal is therefore very easily overlooked. Moreover, the trees are in full leaf and this greatly restricts the visibility into the savanna. However, the most significant factor that

RIGHT In summer the grass may be taller than the leopard.
OVERLEAF Graceful and elegant, impalas are prolific in habitats that suit them and form the basis for dense concentrations of leopards.

ABOVE The first impala lambs are born in early November and a significant number succumb to predation in the following months.
OPPOSITE Whiskers serve no obvious functional purpose but they have an undeniable elegance of their own. Perhaps this is reason enough.

influences the leopard viewing at this time is probably the lambing season of the impalas. Their young are born from about the tenth of November onwards. An expectant female moves away from the herd to give birth in covering vegetation, where the lamb remains hidden for the first few days of its life. This is its best defence while it is unable to run effectively, for the odds of a predator stumbling on it where it lies hidden are very small. An instinct to remain immobile appears to be operative. I have on two occasions seen predators, once a pride of lions and once a leopard, pass within yards of where a small impala lay motionless and undetected in the grass.

When it is stronger and more mobile – the exact time period is unknown – the youngster is taken back to the herd by its mother, where nurseries are formed. The majority of the young are born within a short period of time, so as to glut the market and provide predators with as brief an interval as possible when the young are easily caught, before they mature sufficiently to better effect their escape. Were the births spread out over a longer period of time, there would always be vulnerable youngsters around and their losses would be greater. The time of plenty is thus restricted to a few months, but for the leopard, what a time it is.

It is their mobility which enables leopards to be found. An animal that walks along a road leaves a trail which can be detected and followed, or is seen by a herbivore that raises the alarm, alerting us to its presence. Often, it is simply encountered in person, strolling along a thoroughfare

or resting by the wayside. During the early months of summer, however, when young impalas are easily come by, a leopard tends not to move very much since at any given time it is well fed with no need of hunting, or lying up next to a carcass. Moreover, summer is the wet season, and on an overcast and rainy night, adult animals, let alone their young, are particularly vulnerable. During one such night a female leopard made three kills, and the Eyrefield female was found in the very wet summer of 1996 with the carcasses of five impala lambs that had been placed in neighbouring trees.

Ultimately the main factor that influenced our success in finding the animals was the temporary circumstances of specific individuals. Thus in January and February of 1990, when by rights we should have been struggling to find leopards, the tendency that the Mlowathi male had of lying in the road while his mother was off hunting meant that we saw him almost every alternate day on average. At the same time the Airstrip female, a few months older than he, was establishing her range in much the same area, in the vicinity of the landing strip on the other side of the river. Her embryonic territory was still small and the terrain very open so that we saw a good deal of her as well.

Both animals were very close to the main camp, and therefore even when no particular effort was made to find them, the number of vehicles moving through their areas meant that they were often encountered simply by chance.

Courtship and Mating

The age at which a leopard first mates could be due to physiological factors in the case of females, and behavioural as well as physiological reasons where males are concerned. This is because a female does not necessarily require to be territorial in order to mate, whereas a male, in most cases, almost certainly does. The West Street female was mated at the age of two years and two months. At the time she had been chased east by her sister, and then south by the Hogvaal female and did not appear to be in any way territorial. I do not recall that she was ever seen marking or calling, unlike her sister, who did both.

RIGHT The Rock Drift male who succeeded the Jakkalsdraai male after this study was made.

CHAPTER THREE

One of the Chellahanga female's cubs mated with her father, the Jakkalsdraai male, when she was two years and four months old, and again when three years and eight months old. Both events took place within her mother's territory; the second in fact resulted in a short fight between the two leopardesses. The urge to mate is seemingly very strong in female leopards and causes them to disregard territorial boundaries. From the examples of the above two young female leopards, lack of a territory is evidently no hindrance either. It is worth noting, however, that neither of these animals was subsequently known to deliver and rear cubs. The West Street female disappeared and must almost certainly have died; the Chellahanga female's cub was not seen after the second mating, but may well reside in the KNP to the east of her mother's territory. Although a leopard without a territory may mate, the likelihood of her raising a cub in another female's area is perhaps not very high.

It seems certain that a dominant male leopard controls the matings within his territory. In one instance, the Chellahanga female, who was with the Jakkalsdraai male at the time, left him in response to the Mlowathi male's calling. She went far out of her territory and into that area where the Mlowathi male was making inroads on the Jakkalsdraai male's territory. The two males in fact met, since the Jakkalsdraai male had followed the female all the way, and there can be little doubt as to which of them was the dominant animal. The Jakkalsdraai male was chased off. Why did the female move so far out of her area in response to the Mlowathi male's calling – especially at a time when she was with the Jakkalsdraai male? Did she recognise him, and had she had some earlier experience that made her elect to join him? Or would she have investigated any male that was heard calling? As will soon be discussed, a female appears to actively seek out a male when in season, so it is not unlikely that a mature but not territorial male may end up mating with her.

Finally, the ages at which a female first mates under natural conditions can be taken to be the minimum age at which she is capable of so doing, whereas in a male the recorded age may be greater than the age at which he is potentially viable. This is owing not only to territorial constraints, by which a young male is precluded from breeding by the

ABOVE: The Jakkalsdraai male follows the Chellahanga female during a consortship.

ABOVE "... Here he lay, periodically glancing up ..."

ABOVE "... After a few minutes she carefully descended ..."

presence of a dominant male, but by simple matters of circumstance. A male may wait some time after attaining his reproductive majority before encountering a female who is in season. A female, on the other hand, has only to come into season to attract the immediate attention of potential suitors.

A further influence on the data, naturally, is that the records refer only to the instances when the animals were seen mating; they may have done so prior to this and not been observed. Leopards find one another when a female is in season perhaps as a result of the female's active searching for a male more than for any other reason. Maybe she announces her reproductive status through calling and through the condition of her urine, which could attract males to the area she is in.

For the former method, there is the evidence provided by the Mlowathi male one night. He was lying with an impala kill when a leopard called to the north, and he got to his feet and moved in that direction with no haste and no overt amount of intent, let alone evident aggression. From this it can be deduced that he recognised the caller as a female, and possibly as an individual too. The position from which the

call had come was several hundred meters away and it took about ten minutes for him to stroll there. The female, when he arrived at her position, was found about seven metres off the ground up a knobthorn tree. He stood at the base of the tree for a few minutes, staring up impassively, neither vocalising nor showing any reaction through his expression or through actions. The female climbed slightly higher and vocalised a few times; unfortunately I kept no record of the event and cannot remember what form they took. After a solemn examination of the situation, the Mlowathi male turned and walked back toward his kill as slowly as he had left it. With that the female descended from the tree and quickly followed him, catching up before he had gone more than fifty metres. She dabbed at his face with a paw and leapt coquettishly away, overtures that were ignored by him.

From her behaviour, and the fact that she followed determinedly on his heels as he walked off, I surmised that she was in or coming into season. The male's apparent indifference to her may be a confirmation of this deduction, since it is not unusual, as discussed in chapter six, for interactions between male and female leopards to be violent, and females

often take great care to avoid the males. Unfortunately the leopards bumped into the Styx pride on their way back to the male's kill. The female was chased up a tree where she remained, and some minutes later the male was found a few hundred metres down the road that they had been walking along, having avoided the lions in the confusion, and heading back to his food with little concern for either lions or leopard behind him.

The next day he was back at the kill but there was no sign of the female, which might indicate that she was not in season after all. It is also possible that, having ascertained for himself the identity of the female that he had heard calling, he did not respond to any further calls that she might have made once the lions had left her.

We found the Mlowathi male and an unknown female leopard on the riverbank one morning. Each of them was up a different tree, the female high in the thinnest branches of a leadwood, while the male was lying along the stem of a smaller tree about five metres off the ground, looking very intently at the Styx pride.

The lions were lying up in the bed of the Sand river and did not appear to be aware of the leopards. After about half an hour the lions had moved sufficiently out of sight that the Mlowathi male felt it safe to descend. He walked slowly to the foot of the tree which contained the female, and sat for some minutes looking up at her before climbing into the lower branches, some three metres off the ground. Here he lay, periodically glancing up toward the other leopard. After a few minutes she carefully descended to a fork some two metres above his position. By this time the male seemed to have lost interest in her. Perhaps ten minutes later, the male jumped out of the tree, followed shortly by the female. She trailed him into a stand of grass, where they mated.

That the female will actively seek out a male has already been described, in the instance where the Chellahanga female moved a long way out of her territory in order to find the Mlowathi male, whom she had heard calling, and to mate with him. That she left the Jakkalsdraai male in doing so, even in the face of his demonstrations, is interesting to say the least. If she had indeed recognised the Mlowathi male's voice, it would lead to some interesting speculation.

Mating leopards seem to show a preference for dense bush. This became apparent to me over years of observing mating leopards, while suffering the frustration of acquiring very few reasonable photographs of the event. The difficulties experienced in this regard are magnified by the low posture that the female assumes, pressed flat to the ground, so that unless the act is performed on a bare surface she is likely to be concealed by even the shortest of foliage. How true this perception might be is hard to say.

Leopards favour thicker vegetation at the best of times and although they were often found in reedbeds and similarly impenetrable areas while mating, they were also found in more open situations, especially while moving during the course of a consortship period. I have seen a pair walking along, and mating upon, the surface of a road which they were using without any evident attempts at concealment. So the impression that I gained may have something to it but was in no small way influenced by disappointing photographic opportunities.

LEFT The Jakkalsdraai male fed off its hindquarters for approximately fifteen minutes.

ABOVE AND OPPOSITE Mating intervals can be very brief, and sometimes the pair does not separate between one coupling and the next.

Mating

The act of mating is invariably initiated by the female. This is similar to the situation with lions, with the exception that male lions can sometimes be seen initiating copulation, following the female and pressing down on her hindquarters in a polite manner.

With leopards, I never saw a male initiate the process. A typical sequence of events has the female approach the male, in a deliberate fashion, and growling or purring loudly. The sound is a deep-chested one and does seem to differ from the one used in warning, so it may perhaps be considered as a purr rather than as a growl. Her ears are usually set slightly back as she walks back and forth in front of him in a sinuous manner.

The male is invariably couchant at this stage and she may pass the length of her body under his chin two or three times. Sometimes I have seen a female pause with her hips beneath his chin and knock it up with vigorous upward thrusts. She then lies in front of him, still purring. The male gets to his feet with his ears slightly back and a somewhat resigned expression on his face. He straddles the female and begins a series of thrusts with his pelvis, the purpose of which appears to be to effect penetration. Ejaculation seems to be almost concurrent with intromission, and with this the male usually bares his teeth and rests them on the back of the females neck. At the same time, one of the animals emits a peculiar sound quite unlike the rest of its low-pitched repertoire. It is almost porcine and can be written as "ew-ew-ew-ew-ew-ew-ew", consisting of about that many syllables compressed into about 1.7 seconds. It appears to be made by the male.

This all takes place within the space of about three and a half seconds after penetration has been achieved, during which the male's body tenses; thereupon, he swings to one side and dismounts. Often, though perhaps less than half the time, the female spins onto her back and swipes at him with a forepaw, the male rearing up to avoid her and at times leaping back with all four feet off the ground. Domestic cats are known to have backward-projecting spines on their penises which account for the female's reaction upon withdrawal. I have not read of similar structures being found on leopards but the evidence would seem to point to their existence.

These actions, should they occur, are performed with ferocious snarls and savage expressions on the part of both male and female. Thereafter the male walks off and lies down again, while the female, almost without fail, rolls luxuriantly over on her back with every evidence of satisfaction.

The terms used in describing the animals' expressions and actions in this account should not be considered as a reflection of their actual feelings; I have merely used them in order to paint a picture of the process as accurately as can be imagined. The interval between successive matings is variable but usually – from a subjective assessment – in the order of every five minutes or so. The shortest period between successive matings that I saw was about a minute, and I can remember seeing a pair mating three times in quick succession, with the longest interval being about three minutes. Usually, however, about every five minutes seems to be the norm. Unfortunately, I did not record any exact times.

On two occasions that I saw when the Jakkalsdraai male was mating with the Chellahanga female, the male did not dismount after mating but remained in position. Both male and female sat and lay, respectively, for a minute or two. Then the male began thrusting again and the situation proceeded as would usually be the case from this point on, with the male dismounting at the end.

Temperature may have an effect on mating activity. The Jakkalsdraai male and Chellahanga female were found lying in the riverbed in December 1993, having been seen mating the day before. It was a typically hot summer's day of about 34 degrees, and the leopards were lying a few metres apart from one another, completely inactive. We sat with them for over an hour while the sun went down. When it was beginning to grow dark and a bit cooler, the female sat up, walked across to the male and initiated mating. Thereafter they continued at roughly five minute intervals.

By contrast, the same two leopards were mating at midday in August the following year. It was a much cooler day and they were lying in the shade, mating at twenty to thirty minute intervals. The time period over which leopards remained together when mating (which may be referred to as a consortship) varied from between one and four days. These figures do not necessarily represent the shortest and longest periods owing to the long distances that a pair is capable of covering during the night. A period that we recorded as lasting a single day may

OPPOSITE AND ABOVE Dismounting often elicits a violent reaction from the female; the Mlowathi male takes evasive action from the Airstrip female.

have been longer. The animals may have been mating before or after the day on which they were found and not detected during that time. This applies equally to the longer periods, which may have been in excess of the four days recorded. It is interesting to note, however, that Bailey, using radio telemetry to determine the time that known males and females in his study were together, recorded identical maximum and minimum periods, with an average of 2.1 days. Between one and four days would therefore seem to be an accurate reflection of the time that a mating pair is together.

During a consortship, the leopards can cover a fair amount of ground. This is done mainly at night and is mostly a case of the female staying with the male. Where he goes she follows, soliciting his attentions when the urge takes her. During this time the leopards may hunt but it seems to be an incidental activity, perhaps even to the male who in other respects does not appear to be that much concerned with procreation. This can be seen in the behaviour of the Jakkalsdraai male when he was first seen mating with his daughter, the Chellahanga female's cub. They were found in the afternoon and despite the young female's very evident interest in the male, had not been seen mating.

That evening, as the pair moved slowly southward, the Jakkalsdraai male caught an adult male impala and fed off its hindquarters for about fifteen minutes before moving on, without attempting to store the carcass in a tree. While he was feeding the female lay down ten metres away and when he moved off she followed him without a backward glance at the carcass. The next day they were found about half a

kilometre away, in the Sand river, and by that time they were indeed mating. They did not return to where the carcass had been left. Such casual abandonment of a carcass is somewhat out of character for leopards, particularly since the Jakkalsdraai male, although not lean, was not noticeably full at the time. At other times, I have known a mating pair to lie up next to a carcass, feeding alternately.

Mating out of Territory

One very notable feature of the mating process is how a female that is in season will move out of her territory. This may be while following the male that she is mating with, or it may be in order to find a male. Apart from one occasion when the Marthly female left her area and possibly had a confrontation with the Hogvaal female, and the explorations of derelict territories, these mating forays are the only circumstances under which female leopards were found out of their territories.

Mating while with a Cub

A female may mate with a male after the birth of her cubs. The Trollip's Crossing female mated with the Jakkalsdraai male in November 1992 when her existing cub was then seven months old.

As this happened shortly after he had moved into the area, it is suggestive of a condition of false oestrus. This is sometimes displayed by lionesses when a new male moves into their area. The small cubs being under threat, the females may come into a state of false oestrus and mate with the newcomer, whereafter he is more inclined to accept her cubs.

With regard to this theory, it is worth noting that the Trollip's Crossing female's cub survived to independence, while the Chellahanga female, who also had a cub, may have lost hers to the Jakkalsdraai male when he moved into the area. By October 1993, the Trollip's Crossing female had given birth to her next litter; a month later, she was again seen mating with the Jakkalsdraai male. Here the reason does seem more obscure since logic would suggest that this time he was the father. However, this was not necessarily the case, as she spent a good deal of her time west of the Sand river, which was beyond the Jakkalsdraai male's territory.

Since she was not seen mating with this male on any occasion other than the two mentioned, it is quite likely that her offspring were sired by someone else. One should bear in mind at this point the aggressive interaction between these two leopards when the male appropriated one of her kills (described in chapter six). It is likely therefore that they did not come into contact with one another very often, and that he did not father any of her cubs.

Lex Hes communicated to me a further case of this behaviour; he previously recorded the Sparta female mating when she was with a month old cub. The circumstances concerning the male leopards in her area were unknown.

The Kapen Female

The mating urge of the female is very strong. Very little, it appears, is more important to her than the short-lived usefulness of the male she is with. Nervous, unknown leopards may lose their inclination to flee and as a result be seen. One such individual even became one of our habituated, viewable animals as a result of this.

In January 1989, we saw the Flockfield male mating for the first time. His consort was a young, very shy leopardess who was a stranger to us, and who might have remained so had she not been with the young male during the two days that we watched them. The Flockfield male was of course extremely relaxed, having grown up with vehicles from a cub, and he wandered nonchalantly past and among those of us that were parked watching them.

The female was not, and when he passed close to a vehicle she crouched low as she followed him, looking up at us with huge eyes. Yet so strong was the impulse to follow him that she did so.

After the consortship was over, the young female was seen frequently in the vicinity. For the first two months or so, she would try to lose a vehicle as soon as she had been seen, jogging briskly away. If one stuck with her and kept unobtrusively as far back as the conditions permitted, she soon settled down and could be watched and followed. Eventually she became quite indifferent to us. We named her after the river on whose banks she had first been seen, and she became the Kapen female. One amusing incident during her consortship with

the Flockfield male showed just how persistent a female can be. The male had climbed into a small terminalia tree. For the sake of the story it is tempting to suppose that he did so in order to escape the female's attentions and perhaps he did, since it was an uncomfortable tree with thin branches. He was not alone for long; the female followed him up and a furious exchange followed, the leopards hissing, growling and swatting at one another while the branches bent and swayed beneath them. The precarious situation lasted a few seconds before both of them fell to the ground, where they promptly mated.

Curiously, the Kapen female was also the first female, to our knowledge, that the Mlowathi male mated with. This male and the Flockfield male had similar early careers, starting in the north in more or less the same area and moving south onto Flockfield.

Since young males confine themselves to small areas and often develop regular habits, they are easily found during the first year or so of their independence and frequently viewed. This means that there is a good chance that the first time that they were seen mating was in fact the first time ever.

In the Mlowathi male's case his first attempt strongly suggested that he was indeed a novice, for he settled into position and then, without achieving intromission, humped his way up the Kapen female's back and trod on her head as he walked off. However, it did not take him long to rectify his shortcomings in this department.

The Kapen female was something of a mystery in many ways. These were the only times that we saw her mating and she never reared any cubs. In the winter of 1990 she was seen with a small cub, but only twice, and thereafter never again.

The other females that were territorial and watched over the years mated and reproduced on a regular basis but she did not. Bad luck with cub survival, poor reproductive capacity, or bad motherhood? One will never know.

Cubs

Small rocky outcrops and koppies appear to be favoured den sites for leopards in the area that I was familiar with. These were without exception well vegetated, and had excellent cover for a leopardess and her small cubs. The base rock in the area is granitic, which is subject to a type of weathering known as exfoliation, producing rounded domes and boulders. The cavities that are formed when the smaller boulders lie on top of and next one another can be inaccessible to lions and hyaenas, and within them a leopard cub is safe from its most dangerous enemies.

RIGHT Very young cubs are carried from one den site to the next.

CHAPTER FOUR

Other locations that were used as lairs were dongas and, possibly, the bed and banks of the larger rivers. The Hogvaal female's first litter was found in a system of flat rocks in the bank of a donga, and her third behind a large boulder similarly positioned in such a gully. The Trollip's Crossing female lodged one of her litters in a small koppie, while of two other litters, the cubs were first seen on the eastern bank of the Sand river. The bank in that area is steep and well vegetated, both with large riverine trees and thickets of undergrowth.

As the cubs were in both instances over a month old when first seen, it cannot with certainty be said that this was where they were born and first housed. The Chellahanga female used koppies as initial den sites for three of her litters. These initial sites – the places where the cubs were born and spent the first week or two of their lives – in almost every instance had a secure hideaway, a hole or crevice wherein a small cub would be reasonably secure from large predators.

The Airstrip female gave birth to her first litter at the apex of a small koppie, in a cavity that was almost a miniature cave. Her second litter was housed in the midst of an exceptionally dense and large flame-thorn thicket on the bank of the Manyalethi river. The flamethorn is a creeping acacia which has a luxuriant growth in summer and is well supplied with vicious recurved thorns. The cubs were only heard within this refuge and the Airstrip female disappeared shortly afterwards. From

our observations of her prior to their discovery, it seemed likely that the cubs had been born in the thicket. As a place of concealment it seemed to be very good, as well as being pretty inaccessible to humans.

As a refuge against other animals, it was probably inadequate. Lex Hes recorded one instance of a burrow in a termite mound being used by a young three year old female for her first litter. The cubs were born in a set of rocks and moved to the burrow when they were approximately two weeks old. A burrow of this nature is usually initiated by aardvarks or pangolins, and subsequently enlarged by warthogs or jackals, who use it as a domicile. As such, it is accessible to an animal the size of a leopard and consequently a hyaena also, in which case it would constitute nothing less than a trap for a small cub withdrawing into its recesses.

The cubs in question went missing the day after they had been moved to the hole in the termite mound, and the mass of hyaena spoor around the opening indicated their fate. In the face of this evidence, it might be thought that the cubs had been moved elsewhere and that the hyaena spoor was merely circumstantial. However, the young mother remained in the area, calling to her cubs from around and on top of the mound, which strongly suggests that they had indeed been taken from that locality by the hyaenas.

Leopards do not appear to show any strong fidelity to a particular site through successive litters, at least not insofar as the important choice

ABOVE Secure in the presence of its mother, a young cub is emboldened to curiosity in its surroundings.

ABOVE The thick vegetation on these rocks makes an ideal den site for the Chellahanga female and her cub.

of a place to give birth and house the cub during its most vulnerable first few weeks is concerned. The Chellahanga female used three different small koppies as initial sites for her three most recent litters. They were within a few hundred metres of one another, and all three, as well as three other sites, were used in rotation as she changed the location of the cubs every week or so. The Hogvaal female gave birth to her three litters in quite separate localities, and the situation pertaining to the Trollip's Crossing and Airstrip females has already been described.

The cubs are periodically moved to new localities. This is doubtless in order to avoid living in a lair site which has become impregnated with the leopards' smell, which would attract the unwelcome attention of other predators. The female's regular movements to and from the den could have the same undesired effect. Very young cubs are carried by the mother in the same fashion as is performed by lions, grasped gently by the head between the mother's jaws. Later, the cubs follow the mother as she leads them to the new site. At what age the cubs are capable of this I do not know; certainly by the age of one and a half months they are sufficiently mobile. There is perhaps no consistent period of time for which a leopardess will keep her cubs in one spot before moving them. The duration that she leaves them in a particular site may depend on its suitability, and it is reasonable to suppose that she will move them from an area where a perceived threat exists, although I am not aware of any instance where this might have occurred. Such a threat may present itself

in the form of an unpleasant encounter with another predator, especially an unfamiliar male leopard. The exact sequence of sites used and the duration spent at them was imperfectly recorded, since successive den sites were not always located by us. The nature of the terrain that the leopards selected as refuges for their young meant that they could, in some cases, only have been relocated through tracking them on foot. This was considered by us as undesirable, firstly from the point of view of disturbing the animals, especially the small cubs, and secondly out of consideration for our own hides, which are rather frail by animal standards.

The most complete record that I managed to compile of the rotation of den sites came from the Chellahanga female's most recent litter, consisting of a single cub. By the time it was born, we were familiar with most of the sites she had used for her previous two litters, and so were able to relocate her by methodically investigating them. The leopardess was lactating in early October, although it was not recorded whether or not she had been suckled.

Two days thereafter, she was seen almost on a daily basis at Charleston koppies, either lying up there or walking to or from the rock outcrop. The cub was probably born between the 6th and the 8th of October. She was last seen at this locality on the 17th of October. The next day she was on the nearby Mister's koppies, where she was seen until the 23rd of the same month. This indicates that the cub was kept

ABOVE   "The youngster was a lively little thing, with the dark blue eyes that indicate extreme youthfulness ..."

at the first location for ten to twelve days, whereupon it was moved to the second and remained there for at least six days.

During the next sixteen days, the female was not seen on either of the koppies, although she was recorded on three occasions in close proximity to both of them. It is possible that the cub was located in one of them; however, given the amount of time that a leopard spends at the den site with a very young cub, this seems unlikely since both localities were regularly investigated on a daily basis.

On the 9th of November, the cub was seen for the first time, with its mother on a set of rocks near the two koppies. It cannot be said how long it had been there. Although these rocks too had been well examined, they were very overgrown and the adult leopard could have been lying up amongst them without being noticed. The youngster was a lively little thing, with the dark blue eyes that indicate extreme youthfulness in lion as well as leopard cubs. It was already showing the independent nature that leopard cubs have compared with lions, crawling quietly over and under the rocks within about a five metre radius of where its mother lay. Six days later, the cub was carried north by its mother. They were caught in a chill mid-morning rain storm and sheltered beneath a log.

They relocated two days later, to a small rocky outcrop so overgrown as to be almost completely obscured by the vegetation. I would rate it as the best lair site for a leopard that I have seen, and perhaps the Chellahanga female felt the same, for here she remained for the next ten days at least. After this period, ten days again elapsed without any further sightings of the cub, though it could well have been hidden within the overgrown rocks. The little family was subsequently seen on the 7th of December, back at Mister's koppies.

On the morning of their fourth day at this location, they moved again, to the rocks where the cub had first been seen. By this stage the youngster was about sixty three days old, and followed its mother. It was a great adventure for the little animal, which covered at least twice the distance that its mother did, racing ahead and ambushing her.

The following day they moved again, to an outcropping of boulders in a donga which had not, to our knowledge, yet been used by the female for this most recent cub. Here they remained for three days. Thereafter the two of them were only seen twice in the next seventeen days, in the block of land between the Chellahanga river and the KNP.

On both occasions the cub was following the female. She may have had den sites that we were unaware of, but I think it more likely that she had by then abandoned the use of such safe refuges and was leaving the cub by itself while she went hunting, returning to lead it to whatever she had killed. If this were the case, it would have happened when the cub was about seventy days old.

When the cubs are very young, the female spends a great deal of time either with them, or in the immediate vicinity, where she is able to suckle them regularly and also, presumably, is close at hand to fulfil a protective role should it be required. Exactly how much time is spent at the den site and how much off hunting would be impossible to determine under the conditions that we viewed the animals. Nor could it be resolved at what point in the cubs' development it is left more and more on its own. From its earliest days, however, it has to be left unattended for periods of time while its mother hunts in order to sustain both of them. When it is very small, it has to be left in a secure place; as it grows more alert and capable of climbing trees for safety, which development takes place with great rapidity, it is left by its mother in any reasonably wooded area while she is off hunting. Again, I could not say at which point this happens. It can be reasoned that the system of leaving the cub in a safe, chosen den site is abandoned at the time that it first has meat, for I know of no instance wherein a leopard has carried food to her cub. This practice is sometimes employed by lions, which are big enough to physically defend their food and their cubs. Leopards, however, are outweighed by lions, and the females by hyaenas too, and dare not risk attracting either to a den with a small cub by taking carcasses to it. It is their practice therefore to cache a carcass, return to their cubs and lead them slowly and cautiously back to it, with frequent pauses to watch and listen. Although I have not seen or know of cubs being thus taken for the first time to solid food, I think it unlikely that, at that stage in their development, they will thereafter be taken back to a secure den site. These sites are probably disused then when the cubs are about two months old.

Females can be very protective of young cubs. I was following the Hogvaal female one morning as she led her two cubs, then about two months old, through an acacia woodland with grass about as high as she was, when they came upon two hyaenas lying in a more open space. The hyaenas lurched to their feet and rushed at the leopards. Whether the cubs reacted to the hyaenas or to a call from their mother I could not say, but react they did and very quickly too, one of them climbing to the uppermost branches of a knobthorn tree with astonishing speed and the other disappearing entirely, not to be seen again by us that morning. Their mother, meanwhile, moved forward to confront the hyaenas, who were almost on top of her with their tails up and hackles raised. She swiped at them with a forepaw and, almost in the same motion, rolled onto her back. About a second later, she repeated the action. It was so quick that I was not entirely sure what I had seen, and the hyaenas were either similarly puzzled or reluctant to approach too closely to the claws that had been thrust into their faces and then exposed in a defensive attitude when she lay on her back, for they hesitated. Making good use of their indecisiveness, the leopard climbed a nearby tree in no particular hurry and lay on a low branch.

A far more serious threat in the form of a small pride of lions was encountered by the Chellahanga female. The incident is described by Kim Wolhuter and Dale Hancock;

"Once, shortly after giving a scrub hare to one of her cubs, the same lionesses arrived unannounced. The cubs fled in panic and were nearly caught. The female leopard promptly charged one of the lionesses, who turned to face her. Weight for weight, a lioness is nearly four times larger than a leopard and, seeming to realise the probable outcome of her indiscretion, the leopard flipped onto her side in a submissive gesture similar to that used when greeting her male partner after a long absence. The lioness towered over her much smaller adversary, but eventually backed down, releasing the trapped leopard who fled back to her cubs now taking refuge in a nearby marula tree."

Kim and Dale also saw the same female bitten on the ankle by a hyaena while protecting her cubs, which affected her hunting for several weeks. The leopard cubs' development is far more rapid than that of lions, and they show signs of independence from an early age. Jim Corbett, writing on his Indian experiences, said of the species that:

"... a leopard can size up a situation more quickly than any other animal in our jungles ..."

ABOVE "It was a great adventure for the little animal, which covered at least twice the distance that its mother did ..."

ABOVE Persistent young cubs are dealt with in a tolerant fashion by being smothered.

ABOVE Unlike young humans, cubs relish their baths.

I am inclined to agree with him, for my experiences of them suggest an animal with a calculating intellect, capable of judging circumstances very well. This is seen in their early dealings with hyaenas which, despite the mother's precautions, are not infrequently to be found investigating den sites. From the time that the cubs are led to their first kill, hyaenas are a regular feature in their lives, since it is very rarely indeed that a leopard's prey goes undetected by the ubiquitous scavenger/hunters. Initially the young cubs scramble with alacrity into high perches in trees at the approach of a hyaena, but by the time they are three or four months old, they are treating such situations on merit.

I have seen a young cub about four months old sitting on the ground at the base of a tree and coolly regarding a hyaena as it ambled by approximately four metres away. Once they have reached this stage, leopard cubs appear to seek refuge in a tree only if the situation demands it, climbing no higher than absolutely necessary. This apparent disregard for hyaenas is in marked contrast to the respect they display toward lions, climbing high into the thinnest branches at their approach and watching them with ceaseless intensity, precautions that are also undertaken by most adult leopards under the same conditions. Cubs show keen interest in stalking anything that moves, from small animals

ABOVE A lioness plays with her cub. The tolerance and affection shown by the large cats to small cubs is strikingly evident.

like insects and lizards to their siblings and mother. Siblings will play with one another by stalking, pouncing and wrestling.

In the latter activity, which seems to occupy a good deal of the time that they spend playing with one another, they appear to show considerable restraint, biting at one another gently. A single cub has only its mother as a playmate, and it is heart-warming to see the energy and obvious pleasure with which a small cub greets its mother when she returns to it after an absence. Solitary and self-sufficient by nature, little boisterous and overt affection is displayed by a cub toward its mother by the time that it is beyond about six months of age, and for her part she is by that time far less tolerant of her offspring. But while the cub is still young, a leopardess shows wonderful patience toward it.

A leopard's tail is an irresistible item to a cub. It has been written that a mother will twitch her tail for the benefit of her cub, but I do not believe this to be the case. I have watched a cub playing with its mother's tail for up to fifteen minutes at a stretch, pouncing on it, worrying it and dragging the tip away from her in apparent imitation of the technique it will later use to move a carcass toward a nearby tree. Like any domestic cat, the leopard's tail twitches incessantly under this treatment, escaping the cub's attentions only to be recaptured. Because the cub is very young,

she tolerates the situation. A female can also be subjected to a great deal of mauling, jumping and biting about the body and head. To this she may respond by wrestling with her offspring. This usually involves the cub being imprisoned in a smothering embrace, from which it struggles free to further pester its mother. Both animals may swat at one another with their paws and bite, but very softly.

Climbing is very much a favoured activity with cubs. Once a female has forsaken the use of a den site with a safe hideaway crevice, trees are the only refuge of her cubs, and it should be no surprise therefore that they are frequently found perched aloft when left on their own while their mother is off hunting. Apart from the practical safety considerations, the youngsters do seem to relish the activity. The Matshapiri female left two cubs that were about six weeks old in a narrow, steep sided donga for about ten days, during which time we saw them almost daily. In many hours spent watching them, they were rarely seen on the ground except when moving from one tree to another, and they were seldom still in any tree for long, continually moving about in the branches.

This activity may not be without its hazards, as Lex Hes pointed out in the case of the leopard known as Sticknyawo, who at some time in

ABOVE Leopards are commonly born in litters of two; a single cub's only playmate is its mother.

her adolescence suffered a crippling leg injury. After seeing a cub taking a tumble in a tree which resulted in it being suspended by one limb which had stuck in a fork, his colleagues concluded that a similar accident could have injured the ligaments in the crippled leopard's leg. Small cubs are very able in climbing even large trees of considerable girth, sinking their foreclaws into the bark and using the back feet to propel them upward. Initially they descend backwards, but as they grow older adopt the adult habit of coming down head first. At what age this change occurs I do not know; probably some time after they are three months old.

I did not record the ages at which cubs first take solid food. In an intensive study of the Sparta female and three of her litters, Pete le Roux reported that:

"... cubs were presented with meat at sixty five days of age, although none was seen to eat before seventy two days, and suckling ceased after one hundred and one days."

Predators tend to play more than do herbivores, and much of their play does seem to practise skills that they will use in their adult life; stalking, pouncing, subduing prey and, in the case of the leopard, climbing trees as well. In the past it was customary amongst scientists to look for a purely utilitarian purpose behind play, but now it seems to be accepted that animals might engage in this activity for no reason other than that they enjoy it. By the time that they are about six months old, leopard cubs are playing far less frequently than was the case when they were younger, and have begun to assume some of the outward characteristics of the adults – self-sufficient, quiet and watchful, contributing to an impression that we might describe as aloof.

Male cubs begin to show the wanderlust that is perhaps typical of their sex within the cat family as a whole from quite an early age. They are more adventurous than their female siblings and consequently far less likely to be found by their mother at the point that she left them.

The Hogvaal female's first litter comprised a male and a female cub. On several occasions, after they had been left by their mother while she went hunting, we found the male strolling off on his own while his sister stayed more or less in the position where they had been left. Once he ambled almost a kilometre away down the nearest road. The Mlowathi male made a very long exploratory foray when he was about two and a half years old, moving far to the south of his range and covering about twelve kilometres in total. Almost three years would pass before he was seen in that area again; by then he was a territorial adult, pushing into the Jakkkalsdraai male's range.

A female leopard returns very quietly to the area she has left her cubs in and, almost as quietly, calls to them. The process is very different from the same operation performed by lions. These strong predators march boldly to the place where their cubs are concealed and call to them with a soft, though far carrying exhalation. The cubs respond immediately, tumbling out of their refuge and running toward the sounds. Leopards are in most respects more cautious and less obvious than their larger relatives. The sound that a mother sends to her cub is quiet, and uttered less frequently, in my experience, than is the case with lions. The call itself varies a bit between individuals; mostly it is a very soft grunt, almost a croak. While voicing it, she looks around very intently, alert, presumably, for any undesirable predators that might appear at this vulnerable time for the cub, when it is leaving any cover it may have been hiding in and approaching its mother. The cubs, for their part, are equally cautious in their advance, as will be seen in the following example.

The Tugwaan female's cubs (later to be known as the Newington and West Street females) were found one morning in a stand of clay soil vegetation close to the Sand river. This vegetation is characterised by gwarri and tamboti trees and sparse grass cover. As is often the case with leopard cubs, especially as they mature, the two were separated and did not spend any time with one another, moving slowly around within an area of about thirty metres by forty. Mostly they were stationary; they were then seven months old. We had been watching them for about an hour when their mother returned. She was perhaps forty metres from her cubs when she started to call them.

From where I was, I could see both her and one of the cubs; later, when it had moved closer, the other too. It took the leopards about ten minutes to close the distance between them. The cubs advanced cautiously toward the calls, sitting frequently and waiting; almost stalking their mother. For her part she did much the same, but with less walking involved. Mostly she sat and looked around her, calling intermittently. When the first cub had moved close enough to her that each saw the other, there was very little reaction on either side. They looked at one another as if to say, "So there you are", and settled down.

A male leopard spends perhaps more time with his cubs than was previously assumed to be the case. His position is probably one of

tolerance rather than of active support. Often, his presence with a family seems to be directly related to a carcass which has been secured by the female. In this capacity he is a drain on the female's resources.

Most of our observations of males joining their family came from the period when Kim and Dale were filming the Chellahanga female and the Jakkalsdraai male. All of the associations that we recorded of these two leopards involved a kill, although Kim and Dale, who stayed with them for far longer periods and mostly at night, found that the male and female did meet up on occasion. The male usually called as he was approaching the female; perhaps he was aware of her presence in the area on account of her scent. He either shared the kill with his family or annexed it entirely, the female and cubs moving off. This I suspect had probably to do with the size of the carcass as well as his appetite; larger carcasses might be shared, smaller ones appropriated. As far as I can recall, once the Jakkalsdraai male arrived at a kill, he stayed until it had been consumed.

The Mlowathi male, on the other hand, was once found with a female and two cubs who had an impala carcass up a tree on the river bank. The female was a shy individual and not known to us, and given that she was in the centre of the Mlowathi male's range, where he had then been dominant for some time, must have been mated by him. The four of them were found in the middle of the afternoon, the male up the tree feeding, one of the cubs in the same tree but at a higher level and the female and the other cub lying up under some bushes about

ABOVE The Chellahanga female and her cub returning to Mister's Koppies, one of her regular den sites used in rotation.

ABOVE LEFT AND RIGHT Young cubs descend trees backwards ...

ten metres away. When the male descended and moved purposefully off down the river bed his belly was not filled to capacity, nor, despite the fact that over half the carcass remained, did he return to it. In this case no interaction between him and the other leopards occurred, though since we arrived on the scene when he was feeding up the tree there is no way of knowing what happened on his arrival. The cubs were then about nine months old. It looked as though the male had arrived on the scene by chance and taken a meal before continuing his patrol. In this case he had moved on with a measured, ground-eating stride, typical of the gait used by a male when patrolling his range. To me it was another indication of the difference in emphasis between the two sexes; males cover more ground than do the females, marking and checking their territory. Females work their area more intensively, hunting to feed themselves and their cubs.

Evidently the female is aware of the males' purpose in joining the family and of the detrimental consequences of his presence at her kills, and is, moreover, capable of taking steps to thwart him. Kim and Dale had followed the Chellahanga female one night. She made a kill, stored it in a tree and went back to fetch the cubs. When we arrived on the scene the following day, informed of the situation by the camera crew,

we saw the female walking back to the carcass with the cubs in tow. Along the way they met up with the Jakkalsdraai male who, clearly detecting the availability of an easy meal, attached himself to the party. Led by the female, they kept on a line which would take them directly to where she had left the carcass. After a few hundred metres, however, she veered off at a right angle, eventually ending up at the Sand river. Here she lay up in the reeds. After about a half an hour, the male started nodding off, and she stealthily got up and moved off, staying in the reed bed, with the cubs following. By then it was mid morning and we left them. A similar incident was described by Kim and Dale, this happened at night when they were following the female with her cubs back to a kill. Again the male joined them, and the female wandered around for the entire night until the male, eventually tiring of the affair, left them, whereupon she took the cubs straight to the kill.

I have read in several accounts how a leopard or a lion will tell a cub to stay put, or to follow her, by virtue of calling to it. I have never detected such a signal, but some form of communication does appear to exist, for cubs do not follow their mother when she is leaving them to go hunting, nor do they fail to do so when she leads them to food. Perhaps it has to do with body posture. Once she has made a kill, a leopardess

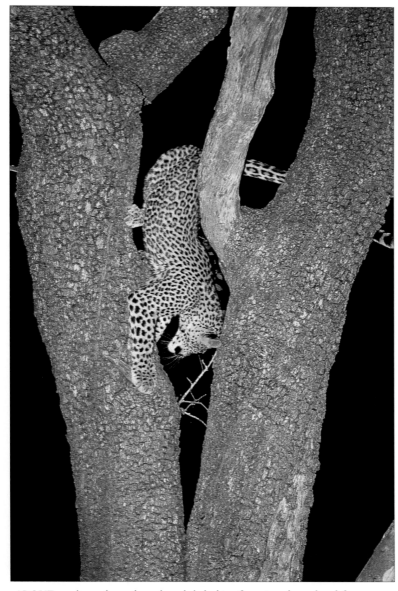

ABOVE ... later they adopt the adult habit of coming down head first.

ABOVE Leopard cubs are quickly at home in trees.

invariably places it in a tree or drags it to cover. She then usually feeds on it herself, and may take a lengthy rest as well, before returning to her cubs. The journey back to the kill is leisurely, with frequent pauses. Even when the cubs are older, between one and two years of age, and more able to avoid danger, this practice is maintained. The female stops and sits down, where she may remain for several minutes at a time, making no apparent effort to listen or look around but being quietly receptive to her senses. The same pattern is manifest in hunting lions, which will periodically stop and just listen, and logically serves the same purpose. While an animal is moving, not only is it less capable of hearing other animals owing to the noise it is making, however slight, but may itself be detected. A hunting predator may thereby fail to notice, or be detected by, the prey it wishes to catch, while a leopard leading her cubs may be surprised by a stronger predator. In both cases, therefore, frequent pauses are made.

No special effort seems to be made by a leopard to indicate to her cubs exactly where the carcass is, at least when they are older. The Chellahanga female caught a four month old impala at 7:00 pm one night, and immediately took it high into a marula tree. She was still up the tree with it, sleeping, when the last vehicle left her an hour later.

Leaving early and making directly for the kill, I was there by 6h00 the following morning, to find no leopards in attendance. After about half an hour, the female appeared with her two fourteen month old cubs following. She threw herself down in a patch of shade some ten metres away from the tree in which the impala was hung – it was a particularly hot day in February, and the temperature was even then quite warm – and started grooming herself. The cubs looked around, not moving much. It was quite noticeable how they concentrated most of their efforts on looking up into the trees. After five minutes of this, one of them had moved into a position from where she saw the carcass stowed amidst the lush summer foliage, and immediately scaled the tree. Her sister lay down and waited. Cubs do seem to know when they have reached the position of a kill. Perhaps there is a finality in the way that the female lies down once she has reached her destination, which to them is noticeably different from the pauses that she makes on the way.

The solitary and self-contained nature of the leopard is distinctly expressed in their family behaviour at food. Cheetahs feed amicably, clustered round a carcass, silently ingesting as much as is possible before a stronger predator dispossesses them of the food which they are incapable of protecting – either by force, by hiding it on the open plains that they favour, or by placing it beyond reach in a tree. Lions descend on a kill, competing for the greater portion through threat, rate of consumption and attempts to muscle it away from their neighbours. Leopards feed singly and in turn. On arriving at a kill, one of the cubs will feed, while its sibling (in the event of there being more than one in the litter) and mother lie up nearby. When it has left the carcass, the other cub approaches and feeds, followed, if she is hungry, by their mother. And so it goes for as long as the carcass lasts, never more than one animal attending at a time.

Once only did I see more than one cub attempting to feed at a kill. It began when the Hogvaal female was found crossing a road, accompanied by her two cubs. She was following a straight line through the bush regardless of terrain and natural routes such as roads and game trails, a certain indication that she had secured a kill and was leading the cubs to it. After following them for about a kilometre, we came upon a duiker lying against the trunk of a tree, by appearances exactly where it had been strangled. It was lying on its side with its neck bent back. The male cub pounced on it and dug his claws into its skin, perhaps establishing his claim to the food. It seems logical that the strongest cub will feed first – in the case of a mixed litter this would invariably be the male – or perhaps the first to see the carcass claims it.

Whatever principal may have been involved, the male settled down to feed, slowly and delicately as is the custom of leopards. Feeding singly as they do, they are not compelled to gulp and bolt their food under pressure from their family at the same carcass.

The delay was too long for his sister to endure. She had been sitting with her mother, watching as he snipped and nibbled at the succulent flesh. Now she got up and, circling around her brother, approached him from the rear. She completed the last few metres in complete silence and with infinite caution, placing one foot down at a time and literally stalking him. The male was chewing on the duiker's hindquarters and facing away from its head, which she slowly approached and, curling her feet up, lay down, chin resting on the duiker's neck, looking at her sibling with large rounded eyes.

Lionesses on occasion use guileful methods to draw closer to a feeding male who has displaced them from a carcass. Lying as close to the kill as he permits her to, a female will crawl and roll closer, stopping when his vocalisations tell her that his patience is being tested and inching forward again when he settles down. In this manner a patient female can get close enough to lie against the male or the carcass; eventually, if his tolerance is equal to the task, being permitted to feed with him. It looked as though something similar was happening with the young leopards, for the female lay quietly, not attempting to feed.

When she was noticed, however, the situation exploded. Instantly enraged, the little male pounced on her and she took to flight, with the infuriated avenger hard on her heels. He caught her almost immediately, and the little creatures spun around in a state of perpetual motion, swatting each other and snarling ferociously. A few seconds, and they separated; the female to her mother, where she sought solace, while her brother streaked across to the carcass and leapt upon it, sinking his foreclaws into the skin and kicking at it with his back feet in apparent outrage and frustration. When his little outburst had run its course, he sat and brooded over the kill, ears back and a furious expression on his face. It was ten minutes before he could bring himself to start feeding again. Possession of a carcass by whoever is feeding on it at the time seems to be something that leopards take very seriously.

The Jakkalsdraai male arrived at one of the Chellahanga female's kills while one of the cubs was feeding. She hissed at him, and he lay down and waited his turn. On another day, when he was hungrier or shorter tempered, he may perhaps have chased her off it.

Younger cubs are clumsy when feeding on a kill which has been placed in a tree, not infrequently dislodging it. Securing a carcass in a

RIGHT A stick is as good a playmate as any in the absence of siblings, given a little imagination!

ABOVE A young leopardess meddles with the carcass placed by her mother ...

ABOVE ... with predictable consequences.

While one of the Chellahanga female's cubs was feeding, it twice let fall small fragments of the carcass, an invariable event regardless of the age and experience of the animal concerned. On each occasion the adult female immediately retrieved the particles and placed them back up in the tree, though they were small scraps of bone and skin, scarcely worth bothering with.

A leopard's hunting instincts are well developed. Cubs will stalk and pounce at small game such as insects and lizards from a month and a half of age, showing greater skills at the practice than do lions. The learning experience that the latter animals receive from following their pride night after night is crucial to their development and, ultimately, their survival. Should subadult lions be cast on their own resources at between two and three years of age, which may happen when the female or females of the pride go off to give birth, they are at best incompetent hunters and undergo lean times until rejoined by the adults. Learning of this nature does not appear to take place with leopards. The only contribution that I have known females to make to their cubs' experience has been to give them small prey items, such as monkeys, scrub hares, and a baby steenbok, which have been caught but not killed.

Cubs are not taken hunting by their mothers. In conversation with Lex Hes, both he and I agreed that the only instances in which we had seen cubs watching, or participating in, their mothers' hunts, had occurred by chance, when the female was leading the cub (usually toward a kill she had made), and happened upon potential prey en route. Usually the cub was a hindrance; consumed with eagerness, it rushed in and put the prey to flight. Like lions, the mother leopards showed no apparent irritation when this happened, but

tree is a skill which they learn from experience, and it is not uncommon for cubs to worry at a perfectly situated kill, tugging and moving it. Since most leopard kills are sooner or later detected by hyaenas, this can be a costly practice. Perhaps the sight of a good few square meals being carried off by a hyaena whose patient vigil below the tree has been rewarded by the cub's ineptitude is an incentive to more careful behaviour. When a kill has been dislodged from a tree, it has been my experience that a cub will feed off it on the ground rather than try to take it up again. Sometimes the adult female may perform this task.

simply gave up on the situation and moved on. A leopard's aptitude in capturing small animals from an early age is quite astonishing. I have seen year-old cubs making light work of the elusive squirrels. The Hogvaal male rocketed up a tall knobthorn tree to catch one, and one of the Chellahanga cubs, although ultimately unsuccessful, showed an impressively mature grasp of the situation. She had seen a squirrel that was lying along a slender branch some four metres above the ground. I was intrigued to notice that the squirrel was motionless and silent, for they will frequently scold an adult leopard with their chittering alarm

ABOVE *After being violently evicted from the duiker carcass by her brother, the female cub seeks solace from her mother.*

ABOVE *The male cub's irritation is still evident as he resumes feeding ten minutes later.*

ABOVE The Newington female leads her cub to a kill, with frequent pauses. At this stage the young male, (in front) at just under two years, is already larger than his mother.

OPPOSITE One of the Chellahanga cubs feeds, while its mother and sister rest and wait their turn.

call. This one seemed to be making every effort to avoid being noticed by the cub, and it seemed very much as though it regarded the small, agile youngster as a threat where it would instead have perceived none had the leopard been an adult. The leopard stared long and hard at the squirrel before walking over to a scrubby zebrawood and climbing a few metres off the ground. Now it was in a quandary. The branch on which the squirrel lay could be reached from the zebrawood; however, if the leopard climbed that high, the squirrel would have time to jump from the branch and make good its escape. It also showed no sign of improving the leopard's chances by moving prematurely. After a minute or so had passed, the cub started climbing toward the squirrel, which watched and waited.

When the leopard had committed herself to the upper branches, the squirrel leapt onto a neighbouring tree, gained the ground and raced for a bolthole. As quick as it was, and as well as it had judged the situation, it was almost no match for the little leopard who shot from the tree she had been climbing in a blur of motion and almost caught her intended prey as it disappeared down a hole at the base of a tree. It was an impressive performance which indicated that the cub was well equipped to look after herself.

A few days previously, the same cub had come across a dead impala lamb. It was early in December, when such small carcasses are not infrequently found, the animals having perished in birth or succumbed, probably, to exposure. The first wet front of summer usually leaves in its wake some dead impalas and duikers, their impoverished condition at the end of winter not having withstood exposure to a succession of cold, wet days. This particular lamb looked to be less than a week old and was found the day after an enormous rainstorm had passed through the area. The leopard seized the carcass and immediately carried it toward the Chellahanga river about a hundred and fifty metres away, alternately running and walking briskly.

On the way she passed several trees that would have adequately sufficed to hoist the carcass into, but did not stop until the banks of the river had been reached. Here she selected a large leadwood tree and, clawing up its trunk, lodged the carcass high amongst some obscuring foliage. Initiative and promptitude she had shown in abundance by storing the carcass out of reach of scavengers and competing predators, but why the long trek when one of several trees nearer to hand would have served just as well; even better, in fact, in that the carcass would have been secured sooner. I believe that she may have been hiding it, not only from other predators, but also from her sister, who was in the same general area, and from her mother.

The carcass was gone by the following day, with no indication of whether or not she had kept it to herself.

ABOVE "... Yet a month later the cub was still around and showing no signs of ill health and certainly not of hunger ..."
PREVIOUS PAGES The Trollip's Crossing female (centre) and her twenty month old female cubs, embellishing a marula tree.

ABOVE Nine month old cub with genet.

The youngest recorded age in the area that a leopard was thrown out by its mother is nine months. This happened to one of the Sparta female's cubs when Lex Hes was studying her. The cub was in fact the Airstrip female, who became an accomplished hunter. The last cub born to the Hogvaal female was thrown on its own resources at about five months of age, when her mother was killed by lions. It was an unusually young and traumatic independence, and none of us gave very much for its chances. Yet a month later the cub was still around and showing no signs of ill health and certainly not of hunger. She was always found fairly close to where her mother had been killed – in and nearby the Matshapiri river. The last time that we saw her she caught a reasonable sized plated lizard, about forty centimetres long, with professional ease, and took it into the depths of a small thicket where it was entirely consumed. Feeding thus on lesser prey and working up to progressively larger mammals, she surely had a reasonable chance of surviving to maturity. But that was the last time that she was seen, her fate, like that of most of the leopards that we followed over the years, a mystery.

Both male and female leopards must learn self-sufficiency, for once abandoned by their mothers, they are wholly reliant on their own skills to feed themselves. The two sexes display somewhat differing approaches to this business, a situation which has its parallel with lions. It is very noticeable in adolescent lions how keen the females are on hunting compared with the males. As they mature, the young females take more of an active role in the hunt, while the males, sprouting the germs of their manes, lag further and further behind. This is a matter of necessity; females have to support themselves and their cubs which, as they grow, place an increasing demand on their mothers' capacity to sustain them.

A male needs only to nourish himself, and consequently tends to display what humans over the ages have regarded as a comparative laziness in this regard. Yet his efforts are not to be scorned, for without fear of an incapacitating injury that might jeopardise the survival of his offspring, he is a formidable opponent, willing to tackle larger and more dangerous prey than the female. A group of subadult males, for instance, that moved into our area in 1995 pulled down five giraffes in one month, whereas a pride of females might be found on a giraffe kill once in every two or three years. As I write, the subadult males from the Charleston pride, recently independent of their mothers, are waging war on the giraffes in the southern part of the reserve. To date they have taken down six. Higher degrees of violence, aggression and risk are the province of the male. His purpose is to fight for territory and procreate with its resident females; a shorter and fiercer life is given to him and it shows in his dealings with his prey. Young female leopards are very enthusiastic, and realistic hunters. They are quick to avail themselves of any opportunity that presents itself, and ignore large and potentially dangerous prey. Males, on the other hand, appear less serious about the business and waste a lot of time with impractical ambition or wishful thinking. Every male leopard that I have seen maturing – the Flockfield, Mlowathi, Sparta and Hogvaal males, and recently the year old cub of the Newington female – has shown a fascination for buffaloes, following a herd sometimes for hours on end. They seem to take foolhardy risks,

yet in the light of the outcome of their actions it has to be assumed that they have an acute awareness of their own abilities as well as the limitations of the lumbering bovines.

The Mlowathi male was discovered one night while we were watching the herd of buffaloes, a resident group of several hundred animals. They were grazing through a Combretum thicket, and he was more or less in the middle of the herd when we first noticed him, looking with great interest and no evident concern at the animals around him. It was not long before the buffaloes discovered him too, and a number of them descended on the spot where he sat. A great tumult and motion ensued. Watching it, we feared the worst. Yet when the dust, of which a substantial quantity had been raised, had subsided, the spectacle presented itself of the leopard supine in the branches no more than a metre above the buffaloes' heads and, fast asleep. At least his eyes were closed, his expression one of blissful slumber, and he did not stir from his rather insubstantial position, sprawled across a few thin branches, while the buffaloes plunged and snorted below him. For they lacked the sense, or precedent, to look above them, and kept circling back to stand directly below him where the scent lay strongest. After a while they gave up and moved off, following the herd as it drifted along, feeding. The leopard slept on. Another evening the Sparta male was found, just as suddenly, in the same herd on a broad floodplain next to the Sand river. The buffaloes had drunk and were moving on and the leopard was

ABOVE Spotted hyaenas have never yet won accolades for beauty; like most animals, however, their cubs have a certain charm.

moving amongst them. His situation was precarious to say the least, since not a single tree nor even a bush was near him. He was stalking behind a buffalo when, inexplicably, he jumped on its back. The startled animal bellowed and took off, prompting a minor stampede. In the confusion, the leopard jumped onto another buffalo. The Flockfield male, as a subadult, panicked two rhinos by bounding up behind them. He had been following them through long grass and his sudden rush, which took him to just under their tails, sent the poor-sighted animals charging off at a gallop.

The Hogvaal male was seen to make an attempt on the lives of small buffalo calves on two separate occasions. In each instance he was sitting in a tree, into which he had been chased by the herd, and descended on account of a calf which had strayed close to his position. On the one occasion he was chased back up the tree by the buffaloes before he had properly descended it. The other time he jumped from about three metres up directly on top of the calf, knocking it to the ground. He was unable to capitalise on his advantage because of its mother's immediate reaction, and was chased back up the tree almost as quickly as he had come down. These incidents happened shortly after the particular males had left their mothers. It appears to be a juvenile fascination, however, since by the time that they were approaching adulthood, they paid the large bovines no heed. The youngest male that I saw harassing buffaloes was the Newington female's cub, at the time a year old. His family was spending some time in the reed beds around the Sand river, as was a small group of male buffaloes. We watched him pestering them on two separate days, about a week apart from one another. Again, his coolness and sense of judgement were a marvel to behold. Once they thundered down on a clump of low bushes that he had been watching them from, and kept running headlong into the reeds. A few seconds later his head appeared from the same bushes; he

had merely sat tight and allowed them to run past him a scant few paces away. The terrain was very densely vegetated with a few open patches amongst tightly packed reed beds and stands of riverine bush, allowing him to creep very close to the buffaloes, who became increasingly exasperated with their elusive tormenter. The young male's sister was not in evidence on either occasion though she was probably within earshot, nor have I known any of the females that we saw maturing to show any interest in the larger herbivores. They seem to be as irresistible to the young males as they are of no consequence to the females.

Female cubs show an early interest and an aptitude for hunting – more so than the males that I have known. We saw a great deal of the Mlowathi male and the Hogvaal male during the last few months that they were with their mothers, and both situations had the following elements in common:

• During the months approaching the onset of the female's next oestrus period, which was also the start of her current youngster's independence, the female spent less and less time with her son.
• The youngster appeared entirely dependent on its mother for food.
• The female only made contact with her cub once she had made a kill. She then went back to where she had left him, called, and led him to the food.
• Once the carcass was finished, the two leopards separated within a day. The cub might follow his mother for a while, but then stayed put or wandered off in a different direction. No effort was made on the cub's part to stay with his mother, or on hers to encourage him to follow.

The Mlowathi male's behaviour in the few months prior to his independence did nothing to inspire any confidence on our part in his ability to look after himself. His mother was operating in an area close to the camp and well serviced by roads, and we found him lying on or close

to one of these roads on an almost daily basis. Whenever I think of this leopard, an image comes to mind of him lying in the dust on a torpid afternoon, solemnly licking the toes that appended a gracefully extended hind limb – an edifying activity, to be sure, but hardly guaranteed to put food on the table. In three months, I only once saw him making anything resembling an attempt at hunting. The coughing alarm calls of some vervet monkeys had led us to a leadwood tree, in the diverticulated branches of which both monkeys and young leopard were to be seen. About three metres off the ground was the Mlowathi male, his eyes fixed on the monkeys with a kind of indifferent enthusiasm and paying little attention to where, lethargically and clumsily, he was placing his paws as he slowly climbed toward them. The little monkeys were enraged, bobbing their

ABOVE The liberty of using one's mother as a doormat is revoked as cubs grow older.

ABOVE The Chellahanga female enjoyed great success in rearing healthy, able cubs.

heads up and down, bouncing around in the branches and approaching to within a metre of their enemy to cough and grimace in his face. It seemed that their bodies were too frail to contain the passions within. Neither before nor since have I seen such a violent reaction from them to a leopard, nor such a close approach on their part, and I found it very attractive to suppose that their pride as professional prey was outraged at the very idea that they might be caught by such a woeful incompetent, rather than that they had felt any real alarm at his efforts. After he had climbed a little higher, the leopard's eyelids began to droop and, closing them on the activity above him, he draped himself over a convenient few branches. He knew where his dinner was; the technicalities of securing it were of no consideration for the moment.

Viewed from our perspective, neither of the two young male leopards seemed prepared for the time when they must suddenly assume the obligation of providing for themselves. But such are the dangers of applying subjective judgements to situations. In March 1990, the Mlowathi male's mother was seen with an adult male, suggesting that she was coming into season, at the end of the month, the youngster was seen with her for the last time. We saw nothing of him thereafter until the end of April, when he was found with the carcasses of a cane rat and an adult female duiker up the same tree. From that moment on he never looked back, becoming a resourceful hunter and gaining condition as the years went by. In similar fashion, the Hogvaal male adapted to life on his own without perceptibly losing an ounce of condition.

Leopards are not very demonstrative to one another, and the affection and tolerance that a female shows toward small cubs soon fades. By the time that they are a year old, she often shows irritation when they approach too close to her. Before the birth of her next cub, contact with them is severed. Female cubs, as maturing potential rivals, are chased off. Males, it would appear, are simply left. The growing intolerance that a leopardess expresses toward her female offspring, which culminates in the youngster being chased and ultimately expelled from her territory, was observed by us on numerous occasions. The Chellahanga female, Hogvaal female and Dudley female were all seen aggressively pursuing their subadult daughters, and Lex Hes recorded similar encounters.

One hot summer's afternoon saw a most entertaining little interaction between a female leopard and her well-grown cub, which must have taken place very close to the time that the youngster was eventually expelled. The female was a somewhat nervous animal. Her cub, which looked as though it was between one and a half and two years old, was fairly indifferent to vehicles. They had been found in the morning with the carcass of a bushbuck which had been killed and lodged high in the branches of a large schotia tree that was growing close to the river's bank. When I arrived at the sighting that afternoon, the

ABOVE White rhino with calf. Rhinos are largely nocturnal, and spend large parts of the day, especially the hotter ones, sleeping.

youngster was up the tree feeding, her mother lying in some shade away from the river, where the bank levelled out. The tree had a girth of several metres and the kill was resting on a stout horizontal branch, on which the leopard comfortably lay, about seven metres above the ground. The young leopard had been feeding quietly for some minutes when she began to growl and hiss at her mother, without ceasing to gnaw and tear at the carcass. These impertinences were answered by low growls from

the bushes amidst which the older animal was barely perceptible, some fifteen metres from the base of the tree. I was certain that this behaviour would not normally be tolerated, and suspected, moreover, that the vehicle was too close to the tree – it was parked about five metres from the base on the downslope side – for the adult to have felt comfortable in approaching with a view to climbing it. Accordingly I moved back, and no sooner had this been accomplished than the adult walked quickly to

number of seconds had passed, the hoarse, rasping call of the dominant leopard came floating back to us. I do not think it could have been very long at all before that particular youngster was chased, once and for all, from her mother's territory. The youngster's attitude suggests that her hormones were starting to become active. The situation may have been intensified by the carcass, over which an individual leopard tends to be possessive in the presence of its family, and by the fact that it was situated high in a tree. In most confrontations with their own and with other species, leopards seem to derive a great deal of security from being in a tree above their opponent. Perhaps her aggressive feelings over the meat, of which she was in possession, exacerbated by her hormones and strengthened by a false sense of security owing to her elevated position, caused her to challenge her mother. The adult animal's prompt and vigorous response, and especially her calling, show that she was beginning to regard the subadult as a rival female and no longer as her daughter.

Ranges of males overlap those of females, and a leopard seems to be under no compulsion to expel her male offspring from her territory. Exactly when she last seeks him out, in order to lead him to a kill that she has stashed, would be interesting to know. This probably happens only when she is pregnant with her next litter. Although the evidence that we collected suggests that a young male is not evicted by his mother, he may well receive a distinctly unwanted message from her suitors when she comes into oestrus. This process was probably under way one night when we found the Mlowathi female and an adult male.

The male was a nervous one, unaccustomed to vehicles, and we were unable to view him except at a distance. Later another leopard was noticed, lurking furtively on the outskirts of the sighting and showing all the hallmarks of being a nervous animal itself. It was and it was not; it was the Mlowathi male, and though nervous of us he certainly was not, with respect to the larger animal attending his mother he most definitely was. He was last seen with his mother fourteen days later. A young male's association with his mother does not necessarily end when he is 'chased out' by the male or males courting her. After leopards have mated they go their separate ways and there is then nothing to prevent a female from joining her male offspring again, as appeared to be the case with the Mlowathi male and his mother. The only reason that a female might have for physically rejecting her male offspring would be if the new cub were to be in any danger from him. Two observations involving the Hogvaal male suggest that this may not be the case. We saw him one morning, catching and feeding off a warthog piglet. That afternoon, returning to the same area, we not only relocated him but, a little later, found his mother as well. She was with the surviving cub from her next litter, a female, which was then seven months old. Her son, having finished his meal and wandered off, bumped into the two of them. The female was lying under a bush and watched as he walked by about eight metres away. Each had quite neutral expressions on their faces and showed little apparent interest in the other.

Just over a month later, the three leopards were all seen together again. This meeting was occasioned by a young kudu kill. It was not apparent whether the female or the young male had killed it, but all of them were quite amicably resting up around it. As will later be discussed, the nature of young leopards' dispersal patterns means that parents may well mate with their offspring.

the tree, scaled the trunk fluidly and effortlessly and attacked her daughter. The youngster fell from the branch under a hailstorm of blows and hung suspended by her foreclaws, struggling to climb back up. Leaning over, her mother dealt her a blow that sent her tumbling to the ground, where she quickly ran off in a scrabbling rush. The adult ran down the tree and chased after her daughter; both were lost to sight after they had gone several paces into the riverine bush. Before an equivalent

Territory

Vacant territories are probably very important to a young leopard's success; most of the animals that we saw growing up and becoming independent disappeared some months after they left their mothers. Virtually all the leopards, male and female, that survived to adulthood and whose careers we subsequently followed, occupied areas that were not known to be held by an adult at the time that the youngsters were left on their own. Female cubs are invariably actively expelled by the mother when she has her next litter. At this point they appear to be regarded by her as adults and as rivals.

RIGHT An adult male leopard scrape-marking during a night patrol.

CHAPTER FIVE

It seems that this happens only when she is pregnant with the next litter, and not when she comes into season again. The Chellahanga female once mated eight times over a period of twelve months, and after each mating bout rejoined her two female cubs, who were nine months old when she first started mating. One might expect her to start considering them as rivals when she first came into season again, and behave aggressively toward them, but it seems that this only happens when she is pregnant.

Male cubs are simply abandoned. Territories of males and females overlap, and the presence of a male in the area is of no territorial concern to a female. The Hogvaal male was seen with his mother on two occasions after the birth of her next litter, and she showed no interest in him at all even though her cub was then only a few months old. In fact, on the second occasion all three of them were seen sharing a kill.

A female leopard's territory probably represents the minimum area that is required for her survival; the main requirement in this sense is prey availability. In Bailey's study the average range of female leopards was just under fifteen square kilometres. In the southwestern Cape, where natural prey densities are lower owing to the presence of farmland, the range of a particular female was found by Norton to be four hundred and eighty seven square kilometres, while in the semidesert of the Karoo females may range over eight hundred square kilometres.

Once she has established a range, a female leopard probably does not move out of it for the rest of her life. This was found to be the case in all of the females that we followed, and is quite different from the pattern in males. The best and almost certainly the most common method of occupying a territory is to move into a derelict one. In all instances that we observed, barring two, this happened when such an area existed on the borders of the territory belonging to the young leopard's mother. The daughters of the Trollip's Crossing female, who in time came to be known as the Styx and White Cloth females, moved further away, bypassing occupied terrritories in order to establish their own. Just how far a young leopard would go in order to find an unoccupied area was impossible to determine, since once an animal crossed the borders of the land that we traversed they were of course lost to us.

Females scent mark their territories with urine in very much the same way as do males, spraying a few drops at a time on trees and bushes. Unlike males, they seem to respect one another's boundaries once they have been established.

An exceptionally aggressive or confident youngster might of course challenge an adult for an existing territory. This could not be expected to happen very often owing to the difference in size and weight between an adult and a juvenile, but it certainly did occur in the case of the White

ABOVE The Newington female rubs her head and neck against a tree. This may serve to deposit scent marks.
OPPOSITE African elephants doze on their feet, and are hardly ever seen lying down.

ABOVE The Jakkalsdraai male rubs against a leafy bush, turns and sprays up onto the leaves.

At the time of writing, the Styx female's subadult cub is giving her mother a great deal of cheek, remaining in her territory and scent-marking in it. This is a quite unique instance in our experience since usually an adult female is pretty brisk about expelling her female cubs. One would expect this to be a matter of course, with the mother having established a psychological dominance over her offspring. The outcome of this situation remains to be seen, and it is a good example of the variation that can occur in the behaviour of probably all members of the cat family. Although general rules exist and are almost invariably followed, making them in most instances extremely predictable, they are capable of very individual and sometimes quite surprising departures from the norm.

The adult females that we followed did not move out of their territories once they had been established, and the borders were remarkably consistent over time. The only situation that led to a violation of existing borders was that of a female in season. The mating urge in female leopards is very strong, leading them to entirely disregard established boundaries when looking for a mate or following a male that they were mating with. Since these mating periods can be up to four days in duration, they can lead to a female being out of her territory for days on end as well as moving a considerable distance away from her area.

A male leopard's territory is significantly bigger than that of a female. It is probably fair to say that it will be as big as an individual can effectively control, limited by his ability to cover the ground and to dominate the other males that he comes into contact with. Females are concerned with raising cubs to independence; they need only as much land as contains suitable den sites and enough prey to survive on. Males are more concerned with mating rights, and the larger the territory, the more females they will have access to; Bailey found that a male may have up to six females within the area that he controls. Male cats are notorious for their tendency to roam, which has of course the desirable effect of bringing them into contact with other females.

This is very noticeable in lions; I saw two cases of male lions maturing within their prides and in one of them to a dominant status as well, forming an alliance with a resident dominant male. However, in both cases by the time the young male was about five years old, he left the area entirely and as far as we were aware, had no further contact with his natal pride.

One might expect a similar situation to exist with leopards, and this certainly appeared to be the case with the Flockfield male, whose territory moved progressively southward. He was resident within a

Cloth female who moved into the Hogvaal female's area and actually fought with her on at least one occasion. The fight lasted about fifteen minutes and appeared to have been won by the younger animal. In the months that followed, the Hogvaal female moved into the northern part of her range, which was in the opposite direction from that in which the challenge had come. Meanwhile, the White Cloth female established herself in the southern part of the Hogvaal female's range, on one occasion leaving a kill that she had made and was feeding off to march into the middle of the older female's area, marking furiously as she went. Unfortunately the outcome of this challenge would never be known, since the Hogvaal female was killed by lions a few days later, but from what we saw of the interactions it seemed that the younger animal may well have prevailed.

ABOVE The Flockfield male scent-marking in the Kapen river in 1988. This was where he established his first territory.

particular area for some years at a time. The Mlowathi male, however, showed a completely different pattern, merely expanding his territory over the years without giving up any part of it. By the time he was in his prime he had a larger territory by far than was known to be occupied by any of the other dominant males that I knew and was pushing into the Jakkalsdraai male's area. During his southernmost incursion we in fact saw both leopards together; the Mlowathi male was walking steadily forward, scent-marking, with his rival ahead of him, muttering in a most discontented manner and growling but giving ground. It seemed fairly certain that he would have taken over the other leopard's territory but again we would never know; a few months after this encounter the Mlowathi male disappeared. Perhaps the Jakkalsdraai male fought back and killed his rival, but we saw no wounds on him to suggest that such a fight had occurred. The Jakkalsdraai male had himself, some years earlier,

ABOVE Four years later, the Mlowathi male was territorial in the same area.

ABOVE The Jakkalsdraai male grimaces on detecting the scent marks of a rival. This gesture (flehmen) exposes the olfactory organs to better advantage.

ABOVE Roads are frequently used by male leopards.

forced the Flockfield male out of the area that he had occupied for two and a half years. Relations between the two animals were thereafter quite cordial, and they marked their common border assiduously. In fact if one of them was seen walking along the border and marking it, it was a pretty fair bet that the other leopard would be doing exactly the same the following day. On rare occasions they were seen together, engaging in what Kim and Dale described as a parallel walk, pacing the boundary about ten metres apart from one another, marking as they went. There is some good footage of them doing precisely this in "Beauty and the Beasts".

From these observations it appears that male leopards will hold onto whatever land they can and, unlike females, are not at all shy about increasing that area at the

ABOVE The purposeful ground-eating stride of a territorial male leopard.

expense of existing territories belonging to other dominant males. The way in which they move through their territories reflects the different considerations at work. I think it is accurate to say that males move through their territories with the primary aim of patrolling and marking them against other males, and hunt as a secondary consideration, whereas females are always concerned first with finding and catching prey. A male on the move invariably walks with seemingly great purpose and often in a straight line, through or along a border of his terrritory. Females walk slower and seemingly at random, often changing direction and even doubling back, covering the ground far more thoroughly than do males in the search for food, a primary directive in the task of rearing young.

ABOVE The Mlowathi male detects a herd of impalas while on patrol, and considers his next move.

Aggression

Aggression is a part of many animals' lives. Males may fight to determine which one will mate with a female. Predators, competing for a limited resource, namely their prey species, often maintain territories from which others of their own kind are excluded. Nothing, for me, so strongly embodies the leopard's lonely, individual nature as does its behaviour during chance meetings with unknown members of the opposite sex. It is to be expected that a male will react with hostility to another male, as should two females each to the other. Similar antagonism, however, is also to be found between the sexes.

RIGHT The Mlovathi male in pensive mood.

CHAPTER SIX

Aggression between the Sexes

In all the interactions that I saw, the female rapidly took refuge in a tree and, after an exchange of pleasantries that was, in most cases, fairly short, descended and moved off away from where the male was last headed. The first involved the Flockfield male and his grandmother, the Sparta female. She climbed a tree and came down when the male had passed by. He was then still a youngster, twenty-four months old, and not particularly interested in the female.

The Hogvaal female met a young adult male, about four years old, one night. She ascended high into a large leadwood tree and growled softly at the other leopard, who was sitting at the base of the tree looking up at her. After about two minutes he moved on, and when he was about seventy metres away she quickly descended and trotted off in the opposite direction. We found the West Street female one morning after having been chased up a tree by a male. She had climbed so high into the smallest branches of a knobthorn that she was visible from quite far off. The identity and approximate age of the male could not be established, since he was a nervous animal, barely seen as he skulked off at our approach. The female lay high in the tree for some ten minutes thereafter, maintaining her vigilance before she began the descent, which was accomplished in stages, gazing intently from every station she paused at on the way. Then she came down in a scrambling rush. She must have watched the male until he was well out of sight, because once down she meandered along in a typical unconcerned fashion. The longest interaction that I saw was the last; this time involving a young male, the Eyrefield male, some two years and three months old. The female was not still for long enough for me to reckon her age, but looked like an

ABOVE "She had climbed so high into the smallest branches ..."

adult, and probably younger rather than older. The male was hunting when he encountered her, and immediately chased her up a tree. The female growled and hissed from her elevated position, and he growled back. After about a minute she came down and ran off with the male pursuing. This took them out of sight. Following up, we found her up another tree with the male below. Here she stayed longer, about fifteen minutes. After an initial few growls had passed between them, they were mostly silent. She was about eight metres up in a very large Jackalberry, moving around in the higher branches. Later she descended to about three metres above the ground, and while at this height vocalised very softly, at the male. Eventually she jumped down and ran off with the male in pursuit, and within a hundred metres climbed another large tree. The male's enthusiasm for this game was evidently stretched thin by this stage, for he wandered off, scent-marking vigorously on bushes in the vicinity. The female then came down and moved off in a different direction. I have assumed that all of these encounters were between individuals that did not know one another, or if they did, that they were not particularly well acquainted, and I think that this assumption is fairly accurate, since at least one of the animals in each case was young and recently independent. I suspect that the last encounter is probably typical of the way in which an adult leopard gets to know the resident members of the opposite sex whose territories overlap its own. Perhaps it is similar to what appears to be the case in lions, where a new male or coalition of males in an area initially chases the females, who take care not to be caught. After a month or so each party is reconciled to the other's presence and may thereafter be found together.

Lions are however more sociable than are leopards and particularly in plains systems where lions tend to form larger prides in order to capture larger prey, there is the practical aspect of group hunting which accrues to a male attaching himself to a group of females. In the case of the leopard, no such advantage is necessary for the male, although he is not averse to opportunistic feeding off a female's kills. Maybe he only really associates with a female, for the first time, when she is in season.

How aggressive are these encounters? The female runs, the male pursues. When she climbs a tree he waits at the base. Lex Hes recorded an encounter with a fatal outcome involving the leopard known as Sticknyawo, who had sustained a crippling injury as a cub. Despite being left with a shrivelled and practically useless hind limb, she survived to independence.

Two years later, at just over three years of age, she was a healthy young leopardess. Less than a month after she had been seen calling for the first time, she was found dead next to a pan. The spoor in the area showed that she had been killed by a male leopard. As far as can be supposed, these were all encounters between individuals that were not well acquainted with one another. Even when a female is known to a male, however, there can be a touch of the savage and unfriendly in their meetings. The frequent contacts between the Jakkalsdraai male and the Chellahanga female have been described in the second chapter; his tolerance of the cubs and of the female, and how they sometimes were gathered at kills, although probably it was mainly the larger ones that he felt disposed to share rather than annex outright. Yet even within this apparently stable association, violence was, perhaps, ever close to the surface. Wolhuter and Hancock described one such incident:

ABOVE As female cubs mature, their mother becomes far less tolerant of their presence.

"A small pride of lionesses had been trailing the female, but she managed to lose them. Despite her success, however, she appeared very much on edge. The male leopard then arrived on the scene. Usually he would announce his approach by calling a few times as he neared, but this time, probably because of the lions nearby, he surprised her. Instead of the usual routine of greeting and then moving off together, the agitated female avoided him, eventually taking refuge in a tree, 'yeowling' at his advances. We had never seen her react in this way, and were intrigued as to what would happen next. The male stalked to within metres of where she was lying unawares in the lower branches of the tree, and then

pounced into the long grass below her. She immediately scuttled up into the higher reaches of the tree, steadfastly refusing to greet him. Not to be denied, he followed and attacked her savagely. He then continued on his way, leaving the beaten female to lick her wounds."

The Trollip's Crossing female's range overlapped with the Jakkalsdraai male's along his western marches. It was an area that we did not often see him in, and despite the fact that she was within his general area and was twice seen mating with him, the two were not seen together anywhere near as often as were the Chellahanga female and the same male. I can in fact remember only one occasion, apart from the matings, that they were together. The female was found in the morning with a subadult impala, which she had killed and taken up a marula tree. That evening, returning to the area, we found the Jakkalsdraai male feeding off the carcass, which was lodged in the first major fork of the tree. The female was higher up, looking down with a degree of tension evident in the set of her body. They growled at one another at least once; I was busy photographing the scene and cannot remember who initiated this or how often it may have happened. When the male had finished, he climbed higher into the tree and lay down; the female lay too, in a submissive fashion. The next morning the female had gone, and the male stayed a day longer until he had finished the carcass.

Aggression between Males

Male leopards may typically be expected to prosecute their mutual antipathies with some vigour. Certainly this is the case amongst lions. A male is in his prime from five years of age onwards, at which point, if he is large and strong enough, or, more usually, part of a strong coalition of males, he may secure for himself a territory by virtue of killing or expelling its previous residents. He seldom lives to be older than about seven, being displaced or killed in turn by stronger or more numerous challengers. No serious fights between male leopards were witnessed in the area. However, all of the mature males that we followed over the years had, at some stage in their careers, scarring about their faces, showing that fighting certainly did occur. How seriously is not easy to say. Two male leopards were found dead; one was an adult and might, according to the evidence, have been killed by a predator; the other was a subadult and was too decomposed for any conclusions to have been drawn. Subadults are perhaps at risk from territorial adults, judging by the number of young males that we saw growing up, leaving their mothers and looking after themselves very capably before suddenly disappearing from the scene.

These animals could, however, just as easily have been chased way by a stronger male rather than killed by him. This happened with the Chellahanga female's littermate. He was an extraordinarily relaxed individual and consequently very well known to us. We enjoyed good viewing of him for about two years when, one day, he disappeared from the vicinity of one of his kills. He had been seen at the kill soon after it was made, but over the next two days, despite the fact that the carcass was being steadily consumed, and that there was an abundance of young male leopard spoor in the area, he was yet to be seen. The mystery was solved when a nervous leopard was glimpsed at the kill late on the second evening; seemingly also a youngster, but slightly larger in size. That was the last that we saw of our friend, and because he had until then ranged over most of Toulon, it is logical to assume that he was displaced by the other male and moved east into the KNP. We know that he was not killed, because he was in fact seen once more, about two years later, on Toulon close to the border with the KNP, within the area that he had been chased from.

Whether or not male leopards might tolerate other males within their territory is hard to say. The Flockfield male was once seen to share a kill he had made with a young male about two and a half years old. The day after the kill had been made of an adult female warthog, both

leopards were found in the tree up which it had been taken. Three hyaenas were patiently waiting at the base, the reason, most probably, for the leopards to have ascended. When we arrived the young male was feeding while the Flockfield male slept, stretched out on a lower limb. In due course the youngster concluded his meal and, seeing that the hyaenas were resting some distance away from the tree, descended and made off. Thereupon the adult male climbed higher and commenced feeding. The

ABOVE Lionesses from the Styx pride in a playful mood.

youngster was identified as the offspring of the Sandy Crossing female, a seldom seen animal, and since her range was well within that of the Flockfield male's, it is likely that he was the sire. Recently, a newcomer to the southern part of the reserve, the KC male, was seen sharing a carcass with another male. In this case the two were much of a size and therefore were unlikely to be related, except for the possibility that they were littermates. Initially the two chased one another, but later shared the kill

over the space of a day. The KC male had fresh lacerations which had probably been sustained during the course of that specific interaction. An interesting observation, illustrating the differences between individual animals, was that the KC male chased the hyaenas off in moving to and from the carcass, while the other leopard was chased by the hyaenas when he moved about. Bailey found an adult male leopard feeding off an impala carcass, with a subadult male waiting ten metres away. When the

ABOVE "They growled at one another at least once"

Aggression between Females

Female leopards are feisty creatures. Several fights between females were observed, and individuals were also seen with scars that bore testimony to aggression on a scale beyond that seen, or inferred, in the case of the males. The first serious encounter that we saw happened soon after the Newington and West Street females had left their mother. They were seen over several months to the east and north of her range, always singly. When they began to scent-mark it became evident that both were laying claim to the same area, and that a conflict of interests could be expected. The outcome was decided late on a balmy autumn afternoon. The West Street female was found a few hundred metres east of our western border, wandering around. As the sun was setting, we heard a leopard calling to the west. Immediately the West Street female spun round and began trotting toward the sound; before she had travelled two hundred metres, she met up with

adult left the kill, the youngster approached and fed. It was evident from the subadult's position on the previous day that the kill had been made by the adult animal. The same young leopard was subsequently located near the kills of three other leopards, and twice managed to scavenge from them. The relationships between the animals involved were in no instances known. This fragmentary evidence suggests that some degree of tolerance may exist between male leopards and their sons, as well as between animals of equivalent size, where conflict would carry a risk of injury to either party. Set against these observations are a few cases where males showed a very marked aversion to others in their area. I was driving down the eastern bank of the river one overcast morning when a leopard bolted across the road and disappeared down the bank of the Matshapiri river. Soon the Mlowathi male came into sight, jogging along after the other fellow with a furious expression on his face and foam covering his jaws. I followed after the two and was just in time to see the stranger, who had crossed the broad sandy bed of the Matshapiri, going up the further bank and vanishing into the fringing vegetation a good hundred metres ahead of the pursuit. Soon the Mlowathi male returned, breathing heavily. He had been lying up on the other side of the Sand river with an nyala kill.

her sister. They squared up, growling and showing their claws in threat and then, suddenly, flew at one another. The swirling melee lasted about ten seconds, in which they raked each other with their talons, and when it was over the Newington female had clearly established an ascendancy

ABOVE "When the male had finished, he climbed higher into the tree ..."

over her sister. They remained in the area for approximately an hour and a half longer.

The West Street female, although beaten and cowed, refused to leave the area. She lay on her belly, baring her teeth and growling at her sister, who was doing a fair amount of walking around about ten metres away, also growling and occasionally scraping. If she moved closer to the West Street female, the latter redoubled her vocalisations and twisted her features to a greater degree, appearing more fearful than menacing. Her threats were empty, and the other leopard knew it. Several times, as she paced about and demonstrated, the Newington female lay down and twisted onto her side, as though she wished to roll over, but always arresting the movement before turning completely onto her other flank. Interpreting this subjectively, it seemed to me to be an act of supreme confidence and contempt, for what can be more disdainful than to expose one's unprotected belly in the face of an enemy? After this fight, the West Street female moved east across the Sand river, abandoning the western bank to her sister.

Two other fights between females were witnessed, only one between adults. The Chellahanga and Trollip's Crossing females clashed when the latter animal was found within the former's range. The fight took place close to Charleston Koppies, where the Chellahanga female's young cub was shortly thereafter seen for the first time, which was perhaps in itself reason enough for her to have given battle. She seemed to incur no advantage from the fact that she was fighting within her territory, which has been shown to be of significance in territorial animals, nor from the protective aggressiveness that might have ensued from the proximity of her cub, for she suffered the worst of the exchange, receiving a gash in a hind limb that caused her to limp for a few weeks thereafter. Another violent exchange that was seemingly motivated by territorial considerations happened when the White Cloth female, a newly independent youngster, took on the Hogvaal female, a long established adult.

The fight lasted about fifteen minutes, and the leopards spent most of the time locked in a clinch, lying on the ground. When it was over the White Cloth female appeared to have won. Evidence of fairly

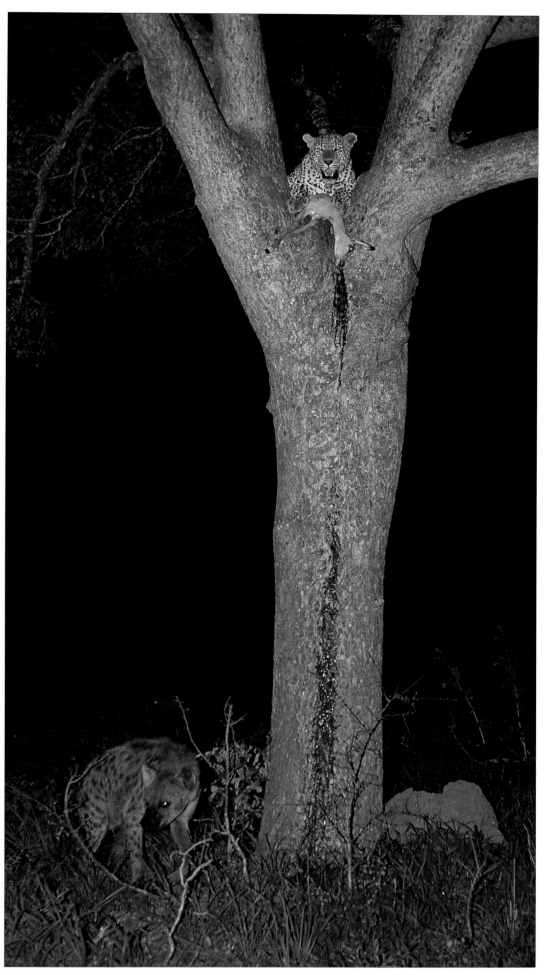

ABOVE Interrupted in his feeding, the Jakkalsdraai male takes his prey out of a hyaena's reach.

ABOVE The Hogvaal male was obliged to spend more time in this tree than he would have liked.

ferocious encounters between females was quite forthcoming in the form of substantial cuts and gashes. Three subadult leopards, the West Street and White Cloth females, and the Hogvaal female's cub, were all seen with such wounds at various times. For the most part they were on the hind limbs, and I suspect that they were caused by the raking talons of their opponents' back legs. It is possible that they were injured during encounters with male leopards, but I think this unlikely. At the time that these injuries were sustained, the leopards in question were moving out of their mothers' ranges and coming into conflict with other females.

Features Associated with Aggression

Early in 1990, when the records that form the basis of this study were beginning to be kept, we found the Marthly female far out of her range, walking back from a possible confrontation with the Hogvaal female. She was salivating freely, which was remarked but little commented on or thought about at the time. Some years later, I saw the Mlowathi male chasing off another male as has been described earlier in this chapter. He was frothing at the mouth which I then ascribed to his exertions, having seen lions doing the same toward the end of a long and fruitless chase after a small group of buffaloes. In retrospect, I came to reflect that the other male had not been frothing at all, despite having run a good deal harder than the Mlowathi male.

These observations acquired some significance after watching an interaction between two young males one morning. We had found, and were following, the Hogvaal male, then about twenty-five months old, when he bumped into another, slightly larger and older male. The younger animal lay down and looked at his neighbour with mild curiosity. The other, however, had a much more aggressive set to his features and posture,

ABOVE Although equipped to cause great hurt to one another, territorial male leopards seem to prefer to co-exist along mutually defined boundaries.

and immediately began to salivate profusely. The two leopards were situated slightly in front of, and to either side of my vehicle. Perhaps if the vehicle had not been present the larger animal, who was somewhat nervous, might have displayed more aggression toward the Hogvaal male. As it was, it became apparent that salivation is very likely a response on the part of an adult or near adult animal to the presence of a potential rival.

A few more observations that were made later on seemed to confirm this supposition. A young adult male which I followed over about two hours while he conducted a scent-marking patrol came to a spot which interested him very much indeed, and spent about fifteen minutes sniffing at and rolling in the grass. While doing this, he salivated, suggesting that he had detected the marks of another male.

In the 'parallel walks' that Kim and Dale saw the Jakkalsdraai and Flockfield males conducting, both leopards were salivating freely. Chris Daphne described to me how he was watching the Mlowathi male lying in the bed of the Sand river, when some monkeys began alarm-calling upstream. He got to his feet immediately and began walking toward them with an irate expression on his face; as he did so, strings of saliva issued from his jaws. Monkeys are very reliable informers on leopards, and hearing them calling is a virtual guarantee that they are watching one. It did not seem likely, considering where the monkeys were calling from, that they had seen the Mlowathi male, so it must be supposed that

there was another predator in the area. Nor was his reaction in any way typical of a leopard that has been spotted by these animals, which they invariably, and sensibly, simply ignore. If it is accepted that the leopard was responding to what he perceived as another leopard in his area, I think it likely that he had very recently encountered a particular animal and that the incident was still fresh in his memory, since I never otherwise saw or heard of a leopard reacting in such a fashion to monkeys' alarm calls. Recently I saw the Jakkalsdraai male in a somewhat similar set of conditions. He was prowling around on the southern bank of the river, where it overlooked a very wide bed thickly grown over with reeds and well covered with riverine trees on either bank. It was plain that he was looking for something, or probably someone, and he was drooling slightly at the mouth. Monkeys were giving tongue on the far bank of the river, and again it was pretty certain that he was not visible to them and therefore not the cause of their alarm. For this reason, it could be reasonably concluded that another leopard was in the vicinity. I find it interesting that leopards seem to be capable of associating alarm calls with the presence of another predator. In Sri Lanka, Muckenhirn was watching a subadult male leopard which was lying down when some Axis deer started barking in the woods. The leopard drew his legs up under his body, changing from a sprawled out position to a more alert one. When an adult male leopard appeared from the woods, he got up and trotted off. Muckenhirn concluded by saying:

ABOVE "The younger animal lay down and looked at his neighbour with mild curiosity."

"When this response is compared to the number of observations when leopards showed no reaction to prey barking at them, ... it appears that this leopard responded to the distant alarm calls of prey as an indicator of the movements of a conspecific."

Returning to the subject of salivation, it would appear that females too are subject to this phenomenon. When I mentioned it in conversation with Lex Hes, he recalled a fight between two females that he had witnessed and produced a slide showing one of them salivating. Bailey described a female that he observed one midsummer's day, on January 23, 1974. This took place on the Lower Sabie River Road, at 5:15 pm to 5:45 pm:

"While I am parked in my vehicle along the Lower Sabie Road, a leopard calls about hundred metres away. Driving ahead, I see the leopard come out of the brush along the road. Upon arriving at the road, the leopard lowers its head and while slowly walking, begins to rasp several times. The leopard appears to be hot as its head is held low and saliva drips from its partially open mouth. After rasping the leopard continues slowly, almost sluggishly, ahead. As I approach more closely to ascertain the leopard's sex, the leopard doubles back and disappears into the undergrowth beside the road. As it walks away, I discover it is a female. Several minutes later the leopard rasps six to seven times about thirty metres off the road."

I suspect that this leopard had been involved in an interaction with another female, considering the way in which she was walking around and calling; her exhaustion also suggests such an encounter, since leopards are not usually particularly active during hotter periods.

Some incentive, such as the presence of an intruder, would logically have provoked her into some form of exertion. Also it is unusual for leopards to call during the daylight hours. Finally there is the case, described earlier, of the Marthly female to be considered. From the foregoing observations, it would appear likely that she had been involved in a confrontation with the Hogvaal female on the morning that she was seen, far out of her range, walking back toward the same and salivating.

Frequency of Fighting

From the evidence collected by us it would appear that females fight more often and with greater malice toward one another than do males. However, this observation could be affected by the fact that, owing to the respective sizes of their territories, a greater number of females came under our surveillance than did males. It is also possible that, while no females were known to have been killed by members of their own sex, two males might have been; but because of inconclusive

ABOVE "The other, however, had a much more aggressive set to his features and posture, and immediately began to salivate profusely."

evidence this could not be determined with any certainty. In the case of one of these males whose carcasses were found, as has been earlier discussed, death may have been occasioned by a predator although whether or not it could have been a leopard was uncertain. The other involved a carcass that was found in the riverbed in a very advanced stage of decay. All that could be established, and that from the teeth, was that it was a young animal; and from the fact that the Sparta male was last seen a month before the discovery of the carcass, and never again thereafter, it was very possibly that individual. This we established some time after the event, because at the same time, the Mlowathi male, who we were then seeing on a regular basis, disappeared, and as the weeks passed the horrible conjecture that he had perished grew ever stronger. Then twenty-eight days after his last sighting, the Mlowathi male suddenly reappeared in the middle of his old haunts. This led us to check through the game report and thereby establish the lack of sightings of the Sparta male, who was not in any event regularly seen by us and whose absence for several weeks at a stretch might therefore go unremarked. It also led to some speculation amongst us on the reason for the Mlowathi male's leave of absence. The supposition developed that a larger male may have moved through the area, killing the Sparta male and driving off the Mlowathi male. Such a theory would account for the facts, but how true it is I would not care to speculate on.

Reasons for Aggression

Ignoring the direct evidence of fighting between leopards, and its incompleteness, let us look at the motives that cause a leopard to contest an intrusion into its territory by another individual of the same sex. Males hold much bigger territories than do females, far in excess of their food requirements. The reason for this is plainly in order to secure mating rights with as many females as is possible. Although a very strong compulsion, and useful to the better perpetuation of the species in that its strongest individuals pass their genes on, the establishment of the right to sexual congress is, in the final say, not essential to an individual leopard's survival. Therefore it might be predicted that he will not fight to the bitter end in order to maintain his claim. This seems to have been the case with the Flockfield male, who was displaced by the Jakkalsdraai male, and moved his borders further south. There he lived for several years more, showing all the signs of a dominant male, marking and calling, and living in amity with the Jakkalsdraai male. The two of them marked their common border assiduously, and though they were on several occasions seen together, did not appear to come into any physical conflict. The extent of a female leopard's territory is probably influenced by two factors – availability of prey, and suitable den sites wherein cubs can be born and reared through the first months of their lives. Both factors are critical to her survival, as well as that of her offspring, so it is to be expected that she will be vigorous in the defence of her area; maybe more so than is the male of his. Much therefore depends on an individual's capacity for aggression.

Perhaps this factor, more than the physical gifts of size, strength and speed with which an animal is born, determines how successful it may ultimately become. The Jakkalsdraai male was smaller than the other rival males that we knew of, and the Newington female smaller than her sister. Yet both of them dominated their opponents. The necessity for this innate hostility may help us to comprehend the seemingly inexplicable aggression of males toward females. I suspect that the hostility that is sometimes seen in their encounters merely reflects the nature of the species. Violence in lions is well documented, and it is a long established fact that new males in an area will kill the small cubs. This has the effect of bringing the females into season again, enabling the recently dominant males to mate with them and thereby pass their genes on. As such it is probably a desirable effect, but maybe an incidental consequence of other factors.

This line of thought began to suggest itself to me when two male lions appeared in the south of the reserve, moving into a void left by another, stronger pair who had moved north. They came upon the River Rocks pride one night; two of the females and the cubs fled. The matriarch of the pride, however, had recently suffered a crippling injury to one of her hind limbs which precluded its use. She was caught, and killed in a savage fashion. The pointlessness of this deed was initially hard to fathom, until I gave some thought to how male lions make the acquaintance of females in areas which are new to them. For the first month or so, there is a good deal of chasing and of running away. The females keep their distance, until eventually each party becomes reconciled to the other and finally associate on amicable terms. Young cubs are killed therefore, not because they are not the issue of the newcomer males' loins, but because, being smaller, they cannot run as well as the adults and are thereby caught. The same fate might apply to an adult female who, owing to injury or circumstance, is caught by males which do not know her and, as a consequence of their very nature, attack her with a fatal viciousness. This could go some way toward explaining why the crippled leopard known as Sticknyawo was killed by a male leopard. Another factor may also have been decisively operative in this instance, and that is the way in which injured animals are perceived by others of their species. Incapacitation seems to elicit little sympathy within the cat family. Jonathan Scott, watching two leopard cubs growing up, related the miseries visited upon one of them, who was limping from a leg injury, by his brother. The signs of weakness acted as a spur on the healthy cub, which tirelessly ambushed, pounced upon and tormented its unfortunate sibling. This can be seen as a natural response from a predator, which should be quick to take advantage of similarly handicapped prey.

An animal that, for whatever reason, is behaving in an atypical fashion, seems also to provoke a reaction from its own kind which is quite different from the simple chasing response that has just been described. Here one can consider the way in which the Jakkalsdraai male behaved toward the Chellahanga female in the interaction observed by Kim and Dale which was described earlier in this chapter. There is also the case of a subadult male lion from the Charleston pride, one of a

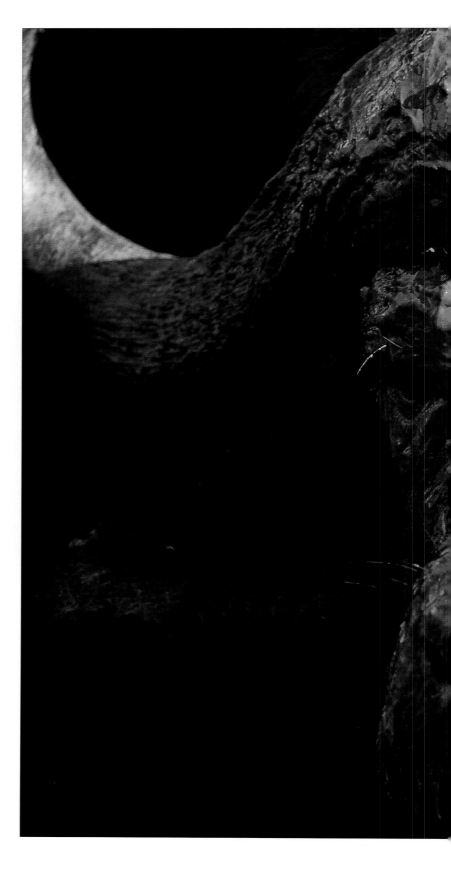

group of eight cubs born to two females, who was badly beaten by assailants unknown. He lost condition and, eventually, the association with his pride. They turned hostile toward him, and finally one day turned on him, beat him, and walked away. I venture the interpretation that he did not look like a lion should, nor conduct himself as one, and so was rejected. A similar situation, though not directly concerned with aggressive instincts, is perhaps to be seen in the way that female leopards

ABOVE Dominant buffalo bulls often exclude other males from mud wallows.

whose cubs have been killed react with regard to the carcass. In several documented instances, leopards have eventually eaten their offspring after carrying the carcasses, grooming them and showing signs of distress. Conflicting urges appear to be at work. On the one hand, the mother is dealing with her cub; on the other, it does not behave or react as a small leopard should, but more closely resembles food. Eventually the one impulse wins over, and the cub is eaten. Thus the situation that suggests itself to me is one of an animal which, of necessity, possesses a high degree of innate aggression. Their behaviour seems also to contain stereotyped responses to their perceptions, any deviations from which may result in that aggression being unleashed. Perhaps a delicate balance exists – too little aggression, and a particular animal may never secure itself a territory, and with it the prize of committing its seed to posterity. Too much, and it becomes a danger to its own kind.

Diet and Hunting

All the studies that have been conducted on the leopards' diet reflect its versatility as a predator. Although the bulk of its prey in Africa usually comprises medium sized antelopes, it is capable of catching prey within a large size range, from very small animals to, on occasion, surprisingly large ones. By and large, the composition of the prey species within the diet of a specific predator is probably a reflection of the relative densities of those animals. This was certainly the case with the leopards in this particular study, with impalas being the dominant prey item, followed by duikers, bushbucks and warthogs.

RIGHT Larger prey animals are invariably killed with a stranglehold on the throat.

CHAPTER SEVEN

ABOVE Bushbuck are found along the river and overgrown erosion courses, and feature prominently in the diet of leopards in this area.

One quite often finds the leopard described as showing a preference for particular animals, which I do not believe is the case. Watching leopards and lions hunting, it seems fairly certain that they put as much effort into a hunt as the circumstances merit, and do not make a greater or lesser attempt to catch something based on what it is. Larger and potentially dangerous animals tend to be avoided by female leopards; for example, only male leopards were recorded catching adult warthogs, and I never saw a female leopard showing the least interest in attempting to stalk a full grown warthog although they could be quite daring in snatching a piglet from the protective custody of its mother. When circumstances are favourable, very large animals can be tackled; adult female waterbuck and kudus were caught by female leopards and the Hogvaal male caught an adult female kudu when he was himself a subadult.

Baboons are very widely believed to be a leopard's favourite food, yet this is borne out by none of the studies that have been conducted on leopards anywhere in Africa. The number of baboons recorded as prey items is in fact very small, and leopards will generally take care to avoid a troop; the formidable monkeys are possessed of horribly strong, grasping hands, long sharp canine teeth and a sense of community that makes the males very swift in response to danger. Only four baboons were taken by

leopards during the period of this study, and the two that were seen by us to have been caught were the result of quick opportunistic dashes; one by the Flockfield male to catch a straggler in thick bush, while the Trollip's Crossing female rushed up a tree trunk one night to seize a juvenile that was perched in the lower branches.

Here the nocturnal factor was strongly at play. Lions and leopards are bolder and far more confident at night; baboons (along with their relatives, ourselves) more timid. They climb into robust trees well before the onset of darkness, where they spend the night grunting in restless misery, squabbling for comfortable perches, freezing in winter, prey to fears of the darkness both real and imagined and periodically sprinkled with showers of urine from baboons above them.

While the darkness persists the tables are turned and an individual perched within reach of a quick, scrabbling rush is probably as vulnerable to a leopard as it ever will be. Moreover, far from being a preferred food item, it is apparent that baboons are not in the least favoured by these predators.

One of the baboons that we recorded as having been caught by a leopard was found in the fork of a large tree. A day later, the Mlowathi male approached the tree, climbed it and inspected the carcass before walking off and not returning. He was then recently independent of his mother and not yet an accomplished hunter, which is not a time that one would expect a leopard to be fussy about what he eats.

Lions not infrequently catch baboons, but seldom in my experience eat them. I can think of at least five occasions on which the Charleston pride, a small group of smaller than average lions, chased and caught baboons. Only one of the females in the pride would eat them, and that literally with long teeth, showing evident distaste for the meal and never eating more than half of the carcass. Turnbull-Kemp wrote;

"It might also be noted that I have never known a leopard touch any part of the viscera of a Baboon, and I have half-gained the impression that these are somehow repugnant to the Leopard, although this is a anthropomorphitic statement to make without evidence."

ABOVE The Sparta male with a young waterbuck.
BELOW Prey can be exceptionally well hidden in the tops of trees.

Brian Marsh, a man with extensive hunting experience, comments that he has never known a leopard to be attracted to a baboon bait, nor does he know it to have partaken of one that was put up to augment an existing bait.

The question then arises as to the origin of this long-standing myth. I believe that early observations in the Cape province, and especially Eugene Marais' best-selling books on baboons, may have contributed to this. He suggested that leopards regularly preyed on baboons and described the process; the leopard waiting in ambush as the troop retired to its sleeping position in the cliffs, the sudden pounce to kill a straggler and the quick retreat from the enraged troop, followed by a stealthy approach under cover of darkness to retrieve the carcass. Leopards do catch and eat baboons – they are mentioned as prey items in most studies on their diet – but they are not a significant food source. Baboons are, however, almost certainly the most noticeable prey item in mountainous regions, and their very vocal response to leopards is far more obvious to a human observer and could lead to an assumption that they are favoured prey.

An interaction of this sort may not even represent an attempt on the part of a leopard to catch a baboon, but rather a belligerent response from a troop that has sighted a predator. Conversely, the capture by leopards of other, shier prey such as antelopes would not be noticed to the same extent.

Lex Hes has a different theory which is probably closer to the truth. He is of the opinion that statements and writings to the effect that the baboons' most significant predator is the leopard, which it almost certainly is, have become interpreted to suppose that the baboon is the leopards' favourite food.

ABOVE Leopards kill quickly by strangulation – the unequal struggle lasts no longer than three or four minutes.

Prey Selectivity

This leads on to the consideration of whether leopards do in fact have more preferred food items. In so far as the effort that they put into hunting is concerned, this does not appear to be the case. Frequent observations of leopards hunting and coming into contact with prey species strongly suggest that an individual will put as much effort into hunting an animal as the situation, and not the prey species, merits. Thus an especially attractive target, such as a group of young impalas, may be entirely ignored if there is too much open ground between them and the leopard, or if the adults in the herd have seen the danger and are alerted to the predator. On the other hand, an animal such as a monitor

to eat it. This train of thought would seem to be confirmed by the findings of Leyhausen in 1969. He established that each component of the feeding chain is independent and separate from the urge to eat; namely the drives to stalk, catch and kill. This suggests that any preference that an individual might have for a food type would only express itself after the prey had been secured, in the form of a willingness or lack thereof to feed off it. The leopards' fondness for dog meat is frequently quoted and referred to, and seemingly supported by a legion of accounts, humorous or pathetic according to the circumstances and one's point of view, of how domestic dogs as well as the odd cat have been carried off in plain view, sometimes from the very feet of their owners. This is commonly held to reflect the lengths to which leopards are prepared to go in order to secure a highly regarded delicacy. However, it may well be that such exploits represent in fact very little comparative effort on the part of the predator. Animals which spend enough time in the vicinity of humans will eventually become habituated, to varying degrees, to their presence. Corbett, Anderson and Turnbull-Kemp all referred to the "village panthers" that hang around areas of human habitation. These animals' food sources include small domestic animals such as goats and chickens as well as what they can scavenge, and they are usually smaller than truly wild leopards. To such an animal, wary but not wholly fearful of people, a sudden rush to seize a foolish yapping pet, attended or not by its owners, is probably far easier than stalking vigilant wild prey.

Looking at the percentage occurences of specific prey animals in individual leopards' diets showed significant differences; these, however, are easily accounted for by the nature of the territories that the animals occupied. Waterbucks, for instance, were only recorded for the Mlowathi male and the Airstrip female. This species was almost entirely absent in the southern part of the reserve, a few being found restricted to a small number of specific localities in the north, which were within the ranges of both of these leopards. The Hogvaal female, although also having a northern range, was found to the east of the Sand river and very seldom close to it. This also accounts for the small number of bushbucks that she was recorded as having killed, as well as explaining why she had the highest recorded proportion of steenboks in her diet. Her range included a greater amount of grassland, well suited to these antelopes, than did that of any other of the leopards. That they ranged on both sides of as well as within the Sand river accounts for the fact that the Airstrip and Trollip's Crossing females and the Mlowathi male were the only individuals within this comparison that were recorded as eating cane rats. Similarly, it explains the higher proportion of bushbucks in the Mlowathi male's diet when compared with two other males. In examining the significance of duikers in the different leopards' diets, the variations are perhaps not as easily accounted for.

In general, female leopards took a higher percentage of duikers than did males. This could be on account of the way in which they move through their ranges. A female moving quietly and thoroughly through her area is more likely to detect, and in turn not be detected by, the furtive crouching duiker than is the male striding through his. The Mlowathi male had a higher proportion of duikers in his analysis than did the Flockfield and Jakkalsdraai males. This might be because his records, unlike those of the other two, date from the time that he was independent of his mother. The hypothesis then is that a young male

lizard may be chased and caught should the deed be easily accomplished, even if, as events seem to suggest, the leopard has no intention of eating it. This might have a parallel in some of the instances of lions catching baboons that have already been referred to. A baboon flees, stimulating a chasing response, or finds itself in a situation where it is easily caught by lions; once that has been accomplished, they find that they do not care leopard, lacking a territory to patrol and, moreover, not wishing to attract the notice of a dominant male, is likely to make much the same quiet, random progress through his area as is a female. This supposition appears to be supported by the records, which show that (between the time that the Mlowathi male was last seen with his mother, which was at the end of April 1990, and when he was seen mating for the first time, with the Kapen female in July 1991 – at which time he had not yet achieved his full growth) of the six duiker kills we recorded him as having made, five were caught while he was a subadult. In analysing prey remains from faeces of known age leopards, Bailey found that the nearest comparisons could be made between the prey caught by adult females and by subadult males. This could be regarded as deriving from a similarity of body size, with males tackling more large prey and fewer small animals as they grow. However, this is unlikely to be the case when one considers the greater boldness that young males show compared with adult females; tackling an adult kudu, young zebras and wildebeests and adult warthogs for instance. I believe the answer is to be found in the way in which the ground is covered, resulting in adult females and young males being more likely to notice small animals, and adult males being less likely. The Jakkalsdraai male was an adult when credited with the three scrub hares that appear on his record, so there is probably no need to imagine that an adult male leopard will scorn the smaller prey items. The same theory might account for the greater numbers of impalas taken

by the males in this comparison relative to the females. From personal experience, I know how easily impalas are noticed when walking in the bush, compared with other species. They are invariably found in herds, wherein some individuals at least will be moving. In addition their white tails, almost constantly working with a flickering motion, draw the eye like a flag. A male leopard striding forth on his patrols is therefore more likely to see, and be able to stalk impala, should circumstances merit it, than he would a solitary and unobtrusive species such as a duiker. Despite, the relative abundance of a particular prey species, the Flockfield male was recorded with several warthog kills while the Jakkalsdraai male (operating in much the same area – and in fact in one which possibly had a greater number of warthogs) was not seen with one.

Kim and Dale, who spent a great deal of time with both males, reported that the Flockfield male always displayed considerable interest in any warthog that he encountered, as well as investigating their burrows, while the Jakkalsdraai male did not. In the Kalahari, Bothma and le Riche found evidence to suggest that porcupines may have been selected by male leopards, particularly by one specific male. In twelve days he made six kills, four of which were porcupines that were caught while emerging from their burrows. Both warthogs and porcupines are potentially dangerous animals to tackle. Perhaps, therefore, the apparent preference of certain individuals for these species is merely owing to the fact that they have learnt how to deal with them, while other leopards in

ABOVE Adult male leopards are not averse to catching small prey; the Jakkalsdraai male with a scrub hare.

ABOVE Rutting male impalas are very vocal, and can draw the attentions of a leopard to them.

the same area may not even attempt their capture, as appears to have been the case with the Jakkalsdraai male and warthogs. Early experiences might play a role in this regard. Young leopards tend to be more energetic and venturesome; several cases of subadults catching and pursuing large or dangerous animals have been described. A successful hunt, or series of hunts, may result in a particular leopard learning how to take down such prey. Conversely, unpleasant experiences may lead to the leopard leaving them alone in the future. In sum, it seems that leopards, for several reasons, are not likely to show any preferences for any particular species of prey. However, it cannot entirely be ruled out. There is the leopard mentioned by Estes, which brought eleven jackals to a tree near his camp in the space of two weeks; they may have been locally abundant or a preferred item. And the efforts that leopards make to catch dogs may indeed reflect their palatability, depending on how one interprets this phenomenon. There is also the case of a male leopard observed by Turnbull-Kemp, which appeared to feed on cane rats to the exclusion of other prey, passing close by poorly tended goats on a daily basis to do so. Maybe the leopard had experienced some unpleasantness in connection with goat owners in the past and had learned to avoid their stock. In conclusion, the leopard is such a resourceful and adaptable predator that I do not consider it unlikely that, under specific circumstances or even under none at all, it may display a preference for or an aversion to a particular type of food.

Significant Food Items

Leopards catch small prey as well as large, and the former are usually underestimated in any study. Where conditions are favourable to their capture, such as in the Matopos, they may constitute a large proportion of the leopards' diet as measured by the occurrence of their remains in faeces. This might suggest that a leopard is capable of surviving on a diet of small animals alone. However, as detailed in chapter nine, leopards have a high vitamin A requirement and this substance, being concentrated in specific tissues, is probably only obtainable in sufficient quantities from medium to large sized prey. In all of the feeding studies that are cited amongst the sources, medium sized prey such as antelopes figured significantly in leopard's diets. It can be reasoned that small animals might be a major food source in the mountainous southwestern Cape study areas. Although rock hyraxes were an important prey item and in the Cedarberg constituted 79.1% by occurrence in scats, antelopes were nonetheless strongly represented. In the four areas sampled by Norton, Lawson & co., they constituted 28.7, 50.8, 37.5 and 32% of leopards' diets in terms of occurence. In terms of bulk, these percentages would naturally be much higher, since they represented the largest prey recorded in the study. In one area, feral pigs were the most abundant prey although the results were determined from only twenty-five scats.

Scat analyses conducted by Grobler and Wilson in the Matopos showed a 20.5% occurence of antelope remains, while in the same area Smith recorded small bovids in 22 and 26% of the droppings sampled from two areas. Again, these figures can be expected to be higher in terms of bulk contribution.

It is possible therefore that leopards may not be capable of surviving in areas where only small prey is to be found, and that the presence of medium sized prey is a minimum habitat requirement.

Scavenging

As Jim Corbett pointed out in the 1940's, the leopard is an animal with varied tastes in food and does not hesitate to take carrion. In fact he postulated that the two dread beasts that he had to deal with, the Panar man-eater and the Man-eating leopard of Rudraprayag, acquired their taste for human flesh after having scavenged on corpses during times of calamity. The former animal, which was credited with four hundred victims, first made its appearance after a very severe outbreak of cholera, while the latter, which killed at least one hundred and twenty five people over eight years, came into being following the influenza epidemic that scoured the world at the end of the Great War. As is the case with lions, the leopard is possessed of a robust digestion which seems equal to almost any amount of putrefaction. Whether or not decaying flesh is preferred to fresh meat is uncertain. This statement is often encountered and probably has much to do with the experiences of hunters who have baited for leopards. A leopard's sense of smell does not appear to be especially well developed, and a decomposing carcass is certain to stand a better likelihood of being discovered than one without taint. Leopards probably approach carrion with a great deal of caution, since a carcass generally stands a good chance of being someone else's property. I remember following the Matshapiri female one morning

when she came across a kill site; where, in fact, we had seen the Styx pride feeding the previous night. A few bone fragments and pieces of skin remained, which the leopard stalked with infinite care, advancing step by cautious step through the knee-high grass. Perhaps ten minutes went by before she had moved the fifteen odd metres from where she had first become aware of the kill, to the middle of the flattened space where the lions had been feeding. In this way even carcasses which are the property of lions may be fed on by leopards. Lions tend to camp as close as possible to their kills so this is a very infrequent source of food. I can only think of two instances where scavenging of this nature occurred. One was an adult female kudu which was caught by the Styx pride. The lionesses moved off to fetch their cubs, and that evening a female leopard was found feeding off the carcass, which was lying at the side of a road. And the Hogvaal male stole part of a zebra kill, which had also been made by the Styx pride, and took it up a nearby tree.

I do not know the circumstances under which this theft was committed beyond the recording of the bare facts; presumably the lions were lying some distance from their kill. Even so, it was a neat turning of the tables from the leopards' point of view, since they frequently suffer the loss of their own kills to lions. Along similar lines, one should perhaps mention here the carcasses which are taken by leopards from other leopards. It has already been described how males will take food from females, as will an individual from another of its own sex. Young animals may hover on the outskirts of a kill and feed off what another has left; this has been described by Bailey as well as earlier in chapter five. Relatedness between the animals concerned may be a key feature here. Bailey's study revealed, however, that leopards in an emaciated condition scavenged to a greater extent than did healthier ones, so it is probably more likely to be a consequence of hunger and desperation. It is probably accurate to say that any other, weaker, predator will be dispossessed of its food; this because of the enmity which exists between predators, and that a leopard will scorn no item of food however acquired. The West Street female chased a cheetah from its kill, an impala, and stole the same. She was then two years old. The age and sex of the cheetah was not certain, but given the leopards' more powerfully built frame and its more effective teeth and claws, I suspect that a female leopard should have no difficulties in intimidating even an adult male cheetah despite the latter's weight advantage.

In conclusion comes a tale which also concerns the West Street female. She was being followed through a thicket of gwarri and jacket plum bushes one morning when she shot ahead and was seen in brief pursuit of a slender mongoose. When she returned to the vicinity from which the smaller predator had been chased, the tiny corpse of a mouse was noticed, draped over the branch of a gwarri bush. Slender mongooses are very effective predators of

ABOVE   Crouching low, the Airstrip female follows after a duiker.
OPPOSITE   Leopards learn from experience to lodge their prey securely, and with great expertise, in trees.

ABOVE Leopards may be the most significant predators on waterbucks, taking mainly the very young.

rodents and it seems likely that the mouse had been caught by the animal which had been seen fleeing, although I can find no reference to their taking their prey, leopard like, up trees. Perhaps it was lying where it had been caught.

The leopard, unabashed, devoured the mouse. If it was indeed the lawful prey of the mongoose, then it is hard to remain objective and not surrender to the demands of our own sense of fair play. Animals are constrained by far more practical considerations than we, as a species, like to think govern us, but even so, bullying a little mongoose and stealing its mouse does seem rather unworthy of a sleek and deadly young leopardess.

Hunting

Most of the animals that a leopard sees, and stalks, are probably detected while it is moving. The different ways in which male and female leopards move through their areas have already been described, and also how this may result in the female finding more animals as well as a greater proportion of smaller prey. It is evident, when watching a leopardess, that she is at times very much more set on hunting than she may be at others. On such occasions she may use trees and termite mounds as observation posts. I cannot recall having seen male leopards

doing the same. In the Sabi Sand, trees are not specifically used to hunt from. In forest habitats it is possible that a leopard may lie in ambush on a branch overhanging a game trail and drop onto its prey. In a Bushveld situation this 'classic' scenario could come about through chance, as the Hogvaal male showed by jumping on the back of a buffalo calf that wandered under the tree he was sitting in. Leopards actually spend less time up trees than is generally supposed. However, they are not uncommonly found lying up on a comfortable branch, especially the females, and from this elevated position, I have on several occasions seen leopards detecting prey. In every instance, they watched the animal intently until it had moved out of sight, then quietly slipped down from the tree and stalked it on the ground. One habit that they do not appear to indulge in in this area is lying up at water holes in order to ambush animals coming to drink. It was in fact very seldom that leopards were found in the vicinity of a waterhole. I can remember a few occasions when leopards spent some time at pans after having drunk, but the motive appeared to be for reasons of resting and they did not stay very long before moving on. Leopards are not very dependent on free water and may go without for long periods in semi-desert areas like the Kalahari, obtaining the necessary moisture from the body fluids of their prey. Watching a leopard drinking was not a very common experience, and in the majority of the times that I saw them so doing, they moved on after having quenched their thirst.

Leopards are most successful when hunting at night. Although far more active during the day than is generally supposed, and willing to initiate a hunt should conditions be favourable, the light factor means that there is a greater likelihood of being detected by their prey. Possibly in recognition of this, they are more energetic at night and look a great deal more determined when hunting at this time.

The night vision of lions and leopards is nothing short of phenomenal, viewed from our standards. It has been established that a cat is capable of seeing under conditions of light one sixth as bright as that required by humans. This is achieved partly by the presence of a reflective layer, the tapetum, at the back of the eye. This layer reflects light which passes through the receptor layer of the retina without having been absorbed, back again. In this fashion it may be registered on the return journey. The way in which a nocturnal animal's eyes reflect torchlight is a consequence of this process. Two types of receptor cells are present in the retina-rods, which register different intensities of light – in much the same way that a black and white photograph represents shades and tones of lighting – and cones, which discriminate between colours and are better suited to functioning in high light intensities; in other words, during the day. Cats have a higher proportion of rods, which gives them outstanding night vision. Their resolving power, or acuity of vision, is, however, poor. This feature is better possessed by animals with higher concentrations of cones, such as birds and apes.

These powers of resolution can be compared in terms of cycles per degree of arc. Cats are capable of distinguishing five to six cycles within a degree; humans, however, can discriminate between up to fifty five cycles per degree of arc. I strongly suspect that as a consequence of their poor discriminatory powers, movement is very important to the cat family in visually detecting their prey. I have come upon at least one account by a hunter who, after violently disturbing a group of lions – through discharging a firearm which led to the fatal wounding of one of them – remained absolutely still, crouched down, and was not noticed by any one of the agitated great cats, which looked at and through him. It also used to surprise me, until I encountered this explanation of their vision, how imperfectly capable they are of recognising one another. Lions which have become separated during a hunt, for instance, often look at one another with great suspicion when they meet up again, approaching cautiously. Positive identification, it seems, is only made at close quarters and possibly through the sense of smell. As it is possible, with sufficient experience, for a human to recognise many of these animals from their proportions, facial features and way of moving, this inability of theirs to do the same is very noticeable. Whether or not even leopards cannot see on the darkest of nights I do not know. Certainly they are capable of seeing under conditions

ABOVE Lions and leopards may kill small prey with a bite to the head.

ABOVE Buffalo calves are well protected. These lions were unsuccessful in their attempt on a newborn calf attended by its mother and several subadults.

herds of impalas standing in the middle of open areas, where they can see a stalking predator in good time. On dark and windy nights, these same areas are traps, wherein the animals would be easily seen from afar. An animal standing in the open would almost as easily be stalked. Consequently they withdraw into thick bush, where they huddle, taking their chances that a prowling carnivore will not stumble on them. The most important senses used in hunting are sight and hearing, with smell being of far lesser significance and in fact debatably of any use at all. Of the first two, sight is probably the most important because it is not to a prey animal's advantage to draw attention to itself and so they are, for the most part, silent. Yet leopards react quickly to noises in the undergrowth as well as to vocalisations. They are attracted to impala lambs, which sometimes bleat incessantly and in chorus, hardly a habit with adaptive merits insofar as safety from predators is concerned. Kim and Dale, following the Chellahanga female night after night, found that she zeroed in on the snorting of male impalas during the rut. And, as with most predators, will investigate distress calls from animals which have been caught. The sounds of careless movements and scufflings are scrutinised, and I can think of several occasions where a leopard has crouched or sat bolt upright, craning its neck and peering intently at a bush from which promising sounds were emanating. Hearing plays a secondary but perhaps equally important role when one considers that a leopard is not solely a predator on the search for something to eat but an animal with enemies of its own, and even while absorbed in stalking something edible must be on

ABOVE AND BELOW Within the space of a month, the Hogvaal male went from catching mice to an adult female kudu.

which to us appear pitch black. They run after their prey, climb and jump around in trees, and see animals, sometimes at surprising distances, under conditions in which human vision is utterly useless. The darker it is, the greater their relative advantage over their prey, and the greater their likelihood of success. Nights of full moon are not to the advantage of a leopard; conversely, wind and rain, added to darkness, are their greatest allies. Sight, hearing and smell are equally useless to a prey animal under these conditions. The mother of the Flockfield male caught three impalas one rainy night, and the Eyrefield female five impala lambs over two nights of similar weather. Antelopes seem to be well aware of how moon and weather affect them. Under a full moon, one finds large

the alert for animals that wish it harm; lions and, to a lesser degree, hyaenas. Perhaps it does not make sense to try to assign any rank of importance to these two senses, since the use of each is dependent on circumstance. If a noise is made, then hearing might enable a leopard to locate its prey; in the absence of any sound, it will be reliant on sight. However, prey animals are probably more often seen than they are heard. Sight or hearing may therefore be used in order to detect prey. Once it has been found, however, the only sense used thereafter is that of sight. As will be seen, leopards are usually extremely cautious in approaching, selecting and seizing their targets. The circumstances are subject to an exacting assessment and this is all performed visually. However, I have on a few occasions seen leopards peering ahead into the grass, ears cocked forward, and jumping high to come down on a mouse that they could

ABOVE Adult male leopards very infrequently catch large animals such as zebras; youngsters, however, can be vulnerable.

only have heard, in much the fashion that is used by servals. Servals are specialists with large ears well suited to this method of hunting. Although leopards are capable of doing the same it does not, on the basis of the number of times that I saw it being employed, appear to be a significant means of obtaining food in this area. Many writers concur in relegating the leopards' sense of smell to a position of lesser significance. Anderson has pointed out how a leopard approached to within a metre of a blind wherein he sat without smelling the occupants. During many hours spent following leopards, I never gained the impression that any of them had detected a prey animal through smelling it. Certainly this sense is employed for the purpose of marking territories and they will assiduously investigate another individual's scent marks, but no great powers of olfaction are implicit in this. A leopard's urine is pungently aromatic and assaults even a human's nostrils with vigour. This leads on to the question of whether or not leopards are aware of the effect that wind has on their own hunting, and make their approach from a downwind position. Although I did not record instances, I saw many stalks involving both leopards and lions that were ruined by the animal approaching from an upwind position which resulted in them being smelt by their prey. My impression is that they are oblivious to the effects of the wind. I do not regard it as unlikely, however, that individuals are capable of associating the wind direction with hunting failure and learning thereby to use it in

their favour. Jim Corbett's opinions on this aspect are worth looking at. Although he had little regard for tigers' and leopards' senses of smell, and in fact claimed that they had none at all, his movements through the bush when after man-eaters was based on the assumption that they were aware of the effect that their preys' acuity of smell had on their hunting and that they therefore stalked from downwind. Moving through dense brush in a man-eater's terrain is a dangerous proposition since one does not know from which point of the compass an attack may come. Corbett reasoned that the predators which he was after, and which in their turn were often after him, did not know that humans have effectively no sense of smell and therefore approached their intended victims exactly as they would have done in the case of their natural prey:

"It would be suicidal for the sportsman to enter dense jungle, in which he had every reason to believe a man-eater was lurking, unless he was capable of making full use of the currents of air. For example, assuming that the sportsman has to proceed, owing to the nature of the ground, in the direction from which the wind is blowing, the danger would lie behind him, where he would least be able to deal with it, but by frequently tacking across the wind he could keep the danger alternately to the right and left of him."

Several factors argue consideration of his theory. Firstly, Jim Corbett was a skilled naturalist whose opinions were based on sound observations

PREVIOUS PAGE Adult warthogs take no nonsense from leopards; here an adult female stares down a young female leopard.

and logical deduction. Secondly, his confidence in this particular theory was sufficiently high that he trusted his life with it. And finally, in a lengthy career of hunting man-eaters during which he spent many months traversing dangerous terrain, he survived, while the experienced and canny animals whose skills were pitted against his own did not.

In general, the animals that I watched were cautious and conservative in their stalks. As soon as a leopard has been detected by the animals that it is stalking, the hunt is effectively over. Most of the daylight stalks that I saw ended in this fashion, with little apparent frustration evident on the leopards' part, regardless of how much time it had already invested in the hunt. The same applied to the few incidents when a cub was present with its mother, and foiled her attempt with its enthusiastic interference; the adult simply relaxed and moved on. The work of Lex Hes and Pete le Roux, based on intensive observations on a particular female, as well as Bailey's data obtained from radio monitoring, concur in establishing that a leopard makes a large kill about once a week. A great number of abortive or abandoned attempts must therefore be experienced during that time. The technique that I saw most used was to wait, motionless, until the prey had moved on out of the leopard's sight. Then it was carefully followed up on until it was once more in view. In this way, waiting when the terrain did not permit a closer approach and stalking up when it did, a leopard might draw ever closer to its intended victim. Lex Hes watched leopards moving around and ahead of their prey in order to set up an ambush, but I did not see this method used to any great extent.

The speed of stalking seems to be related to the age of the animal, older individuals showing great patience while younger animals, especially young females, are more inclined to rush in and take their chances, and move on to the next opportunity if they fail. We saw the Airstrip female catch a duiker one winter's morning when she was twenty-two months old. We were following her across fairly open ground, peppered with dry acacias from which the leaves had been shed, when her attention was taken by two duikers that were running around fighting some forty metres away from her. As they moved away from her she ran forward by twenty metres or so, across open space devoid of grass cover, and pressed herself flat to the ground. When the duikers returned on their next pass they virtually ran onto her and she made an easy kill.

Young females are the most exciting animals to follow. Most of the kills that I saw were made while following the Airstrip and West Street females, when they had recently left their mothers. Both of these animals moved quickly on the hunt, sometimes breaking into a jog when game was scarce. Young male leopards do not show the same enthusiasm. Leopards appear to be highly selective of circumstance, and of target, should the prey be in a herd. I have seen animals get close enough to their prey that an attack could seemingly easily have been launched, yet do nothing. A young female was found one afternoon near the bank of the river, toward which a small herd of impalas was headed. She saw them when they were about thirty metres off, and crouched down. By design or through chance, she was lying next to the game trail that the impalas were walking along and the lead animal passed within a metre or so of her. She was looking up at them intently, but let the first few animals go past before jumping up and making an easy kill. In at least two other instances I have seen a leopard get well within range of a herd of impalas and do nothing when the animals, detecting the predator, suddenly scattered. A calculating precision appears to be operative; given the risk of injury that is always present during an attack, this makes sense.

The final attack is usually made in the form of a pounce or a short rush. Small animals seem to be a general exception to this; I have seen several scrub hares chased for up to fifty metres. This would suggest that a leopard knows that it is capable, given time, of overhauling a smaller animal. A similar appreciation of relative speeds appears to exist in lions, which I saw chasing warthogs over long distances on several occasions, and catching them. Bailey watched a female leopard chasing an impala lamb for a hundred metres in broad daylight. Only once did I see a larger animal chased for any distance; the leopard was briefly seen and was a female, probably a young one. She raced at an impala which doubled back in the direction she had come from and, trying to cut it off, went sprawling on her back. She was up again in an instant and tore off after it, running a further twenty odd metres before giving up. In total she covered perhaps thirty metres, an unusually long chase.

Leopards appear, when stalking, to get as close as is absolutely possible to their prey. Under ideal circumstances, therefore, their preferred method of capture is probably a single bound or pounce, as was performed by the Sparta male one moonlit night. He was moving through savannah well dotted with acacia trees when he stopped and looked intently ahead toward a fallen tree about fifteen metres away. It transpired that a waterbuck calf was lying amongst

OPPOSITE AND ABOVE The West Street female carries a hare she has caught and releases it in the hope of further sport; finally it is plucked and devoured.

ABOVE *Right hook. This is an instance where play is of definite use in refining skills that will be required in adult life.*

the grass and the branches of the tree, on the further side from the leopard. He stalked slowly forward, taking about ten minutes to cover the distance until he sat on the far side of the tree, looking into the tangled vegetation. With the moon we were able to follow his movements closely, especially using a good pair of binoculars. He must have sat a further ten minutes trying to make out exactly where his prey was located, although it may have been less as time passes very slowly under such circumstances. Maybe the waterbuck moved, or it could be that he eventually made it out. However, having finally pinpointed it, the leopard suddenly sprang, jumping perhaps a metre and a half up and three metres forward, to come down on his prey. This type of pouncing attack is also used, as has been earlier described, when hunting small animals that are only heard, in long grass. It was also used by the Airstrip female when she was being followed one evening through tall summer grass. She suddenly stopped and cocked her head forward, then leapt up to come down about two metres ahead of her, jumped forward again, landing on something that squealed, and the next instant scrambled up a tree holding a steenbok by the neck.

A short chase may also be employed if the leopard can get close enough. The Mlowathi male carefully stalked a bushbuck that was quietly feeding in some reeds on the river bank one morning. The bushbuck was facing away from him when he began his hunt, and he slowly crept to within about three metres of it. When he rushed at it,

the bushbuck reacted instantly, bolting away from the noise behind it. There was a stump in between the leopard and his prey, around which he was obliged to make a slight dog-leg, and were it not for this I believe he would have caught the bushbuck, for he only just failed to make contact. Kim and Dale, however, noticed that male leopards were inclined to chase their prey for longer distances than were females. Dale described to me how the Flockfield male once charged at a herd of impalas from about forty metres out, slapped a youngster down and, in the confusion, made a second kill.

The 'classic' perception of the leopard appears to be as a stalker/pouncer. In well vegetated areas, this method is perhaps best suited to the circumstances. In the Kalahari, however, the open semi-desert conditions dictate a very different approach. Here Bothma and le Riche found that the mean chase distance for male leopards was 66.3 metres, and for females 63.7 metres. The maximum recorded distances were four hundred and fifty metres for a male, and three hundred metres for a female. This shows how remarkably adaptable the leopard is, and how capable it is of surviving in just about any type of habitat within its range.

Larger prey animals are usually grappled with the claws of the fore limbs, the throat being encompassed by the jaws at the earliest convenience. Smaller prey may be pinned down by a paw or caught in the jaws. In one case where I saw a scrub hare being caught, the leopard 'crowded' it with forelimbs spread out in an embracing fashion, ducking her head to make the catch against her chest. Stealth and forthrightness, employed singly or in combination, are used when hunting warthogs. In the incidents that we saw, females were very cautious not to risk contact with adult pigs, whereas on two occasions young male leopards showed an unhealthy disregard for adults, and once fearlessly tackled the same. A warthog usually has several burrows in its area, commonly in the form of holes in termite mounds that were originally delved by plundering aardvarks and pangolins, and which the pig has further enlarged with its blunt upper tusks. Within these excavations the short-sighted animals spend the nights in safety, prudently descending tail foremost in order to meet any threats with their knife-sharp lower tusks. As an almost absolute rule, no predator will risk descending an occupied burrow. There is at least one documented case on record of a male lion having been killed by a warthog that lacerated its throat. However, one night I watched the Newington female going down two burrows in quick succession, and exiting them faster than she had descended. She was then recently independent and I never saw her, or any other leopard at any other time, doing so again. Probably, the extremely quick reflexes that leopards possess saved her from being injured. This sort of bold action is out of character with what was generally seen to be the case for female

ABOVE A cane rat leaves a sinuous track as it sways from side to side when carried by a leopard.

ABOVE Carcasses are sometimes moved from one tree to another.

leopards, but was perhaps owing to the greater energy and enthusiasm that young females display. Lex Hes has recorded young leopards going down burrows and sometimes emerging with a piglet. We have seen female leopards snatching piglets from the company of their mothers. The Airstrip female once lay in ambush while a family of pigs grazed in her direction. When they were almost on her, she sprang up and grabbed a piglet in a single bound, and with the next leapt onto a tree trunk with the infuriated female warthog rushing around at the base.

A similar incident that took place before I arrived at the reserve was described to me. In this case the piglets were suckling from their mother when one was seized and taken up a nearby tree. The tree leaned backward and the leopard was unable to climb, with its burden, into the branches, so she hung onto the trunk until the adult pig had left with her remaining youngsters. Then she descended and killed the piglet. Adult warthogs are not to be taken lightly, as both the Flockfield and the Mlowathi males found out when they were youngsters. The Flockfield male, at twenty-three months of age, was stalking a family of pigs through fairly short but dense early winter grass. When he was about three metres away he rushed at them and made an easy capture of one of the piglets. The rest of the family was running around in general panic, which in the case of the mother lasted only as long as it took her

ABOVE The West Street female stares intently at a herd of impalas, waiting for them to move out of sight before stalking.

to realise that a leopard had caught one of her piglets – perhaps two seconds at most. Then she charged at the leopard and gored him, making him drop the piglet and jump onto the stem of a fallen tree which was conveniently close to hand. A few seconds later the warthog ran off, followed by her brood. The one that the leopard had caught, however, was grievously hurt and staggering around in a wide half circle. After a cool, assessing glance in the direction of its mother, the Flockfield male sprang lightly off his perch and reclaimed his prey. The female pig had inflicted a gash in his flank about six centimetres long, which became infected and swelled up for a week before subsiding and disappearing. The Mlowathi male caught a piglet from a family group; however, it squealed so loudly that its mother returned and hit the leopard in the ribs with her broad flat head, causing him to stagger back and drop the piglet. It too had sustained an injury and, following up a few minutes later, the leopard found it wandering aimlessly on its own and secured an easy capture. Again the piglet squealed and, perhaps anticipating a response from its mother, the Mlowathi male dropped it. This happened close to a burrow, which the piglet crept into and disappeared. The young leopard thereafter camped in the vicinity, making from time to time brief forays down the hole but seldom going further in than past his

forequarters. Finally, eighteen hours after having first caught the piglet, he disappeared entirely down the burrow and emerged with the warthog, then barely alive. A few months prior to this, the Mlowathi male had caught an adult warthog. The capture was made at night and was not seen and the subsequent struggle lasted about twenty minutes, during which he was at some risk from the tusks of the furiously struggling pig. Finally he subdued it and rested, panting deeply. His efforts were to no avail, for the noise had attracted a pride of lions, which chased him off and dispossessed him of his hard-won food.

The only other incident wherein an adult warthog was seen being caught happened when the Flockfield male was a seasoned six year old adult. He was walking along early one cold winter's morning when he happened across the burrow of a pig set halfway up a termite mound. This is the only type of circumstance that I can think of in which a leopard's sense of smell might play any part. Occupied warthog burrows have a rank smell around the entrance, which probably alerts a leopard or a lion to the fact that there are pigs within. When following lions, for instance, it is noticeable how they will investigate some burrows and totally ignore others. The pigs within do, however, often give voice to rumbles and glottal growling in response to activity outside their burrow, which suggests that hearing may play a part. Given the strength of their odour, however, which even a human nose can detect, they are probably smelt out first. The Flockfield male climbed the mound from the side which was closest to him, and opposite to that wherein the entrance to the burrow was situated. He took up station on the top and waited. After an hour, the pigs began to emerge into the brisk winter air, slowly and suspiciously as is their custom. The lead pig's head emerged and looked around for a cautious minute or so before it scrambled out. The leopard jumped down as the rush began and caught the second pig in line, an adult female, as it was leaving the burrow. The pig promptly retreated, dragging the leopard halfway down before his back feet, bracing the sides of the burrow's entrance, gave him the ability to resist. For several long minutes he remained there, just his hindquarters and tail outside, before the warthog weakened from the grip that he had on its throat and was dragged out. A warthog's distress call is piercingly loud and inclined to attract predators from far afield as well as, in the case of juvenile pigs, assistance from their mothers. Both of these phenomena may explain why the Mlowathi male, several years after he had been charged by an enraged mother pig, was found with a struggling warthog halfway up a tree. We had lost him one night in dense summer growth dissected by a few rocky dongas, and were following up when the the screams of a freshly caught warthog sounded about eighty metres away in the darkness. Arriving at the scene less than a minute later, we found the leopard in a marula tree, holding a juvenile warthog about twenty months old in his jaws. The pig was struggling feebly but the leopard was in an uncomfortable position and gradually slipping down the trunk. Eventually he was obliged to descend and proceeded to throttle the pig on the ground, keeping an ear cocked for intruders. Two hyaenas ran up not very long thereafter, and the leopard immediately took his prey up the tree again.

Live animals were taken up trees on several other occasions. The Airstrip female ascended with the steenbok mentioned earlier in this chapter, and stood in a fork grasping the little antelope by the back of the neck. The steenbok was kicking violently, sometimes swinging out horizontally, until she changed her grip and strangled it. The West Street female caught an adult impala late one afternoon. Just after she had killed it, five subadult male lions, attracted by the alarm calls made by the rest of the herd, arrived and stole and consumed her meal. She retreated a prudent few hundred metres and groomed herself thoroughly before continuing. Later that same night, she caught a subadult impala and this time took no chances, climbing a tree immediately. She strangled it at the first major fork before climbing higher and lodging it in the smaller branches. The White Cloth female spent some time killing a duiker in similar fashion. She

climbed a tree while it was still kicking, being held by the back of the neck, and soon thereafter dropped it, retrieved it and took it aloft again where it was finally killed. These prompt ascensions with live prey are perhaps inspired by memories of having lost fresh kills to hyaenas.

Prey animals in trees were caught by sudden, swift rushes up the trunks. Monkeys, a baboon and even a squirrel were caught by this method, showing how agile and quick a leopard can be. The largest prey items recorded were two adult female kudus and an adult female waterbuck. Only one was seen being caught, a kudu that was captured by the Hogvaal male. He was moving along the slope on the northern bank of the Hogvaal donga, when he detected a small group of kudus and, as they were walking out of a tributary, came from behind and

ABOVE "... we found the leopard in a marula tree, holding a juvenile warthog ..."

ABOVE "This time she took no chances, climbing a tree immediately."

jumped onto the back of one of the females. They rolled back into the depression, where he killed the kudu with a stranglehold round the neck. The largest animal that has been reliably recorded as a leopard's prey is an adult male eland. The carcass was shown to Elliot (related in Kingdon), who established the sequence of events through backtracking the movements of the herd it had been taken from:

"The leopard had jumped on to this eland bull from a tree above the track, and the victim had at once dashed downhill. The eland had fallen twice but managed to get on to its feet again. But on a third occasion the leopard had succeeded in holding the animal down and finally killed it. In the downhill rush and the whole struggle the leopard had lost a lot of hair on trees and bushes. It seemed that the leopard had managed to kill the eland by biting into the windpipe area, and suffocation was thought to be the main cause of death. Damage to the eland's neck vertebrae must have occurred during its repeated falls. While the only teeth marks were in the eland's throat, there were many claw marks on the flank, and it seemed that the leopard had been on top of the eland all the way down. The warden put half the eland carcass in a nearby tree and – on the following evening – spotted the biggest leopard he had ever seen, with its left forehead all bare and bloody. From the evidence it was certain that this leopard had killed the bull eland without assistance."

Prey Strategies

The reaction of prey animals to a leopard may vary according to species and to its environment. Bushbucks, for instance, will remain absolutely still until they have been seen, whereupon they dash off giving voice to a few barks. This strategy is well suited to the thick bush that they favour.

In this environment where visibility is usually very poor, it makes sense to remain unseen for as long as is possible. An animal that runs from a predator, and loses sight of it, might then be stalked by that predator and, in the dense bush, be at a disadvantage. Therefore bushbuck tend to wait until detected or until the predator is dangerously close before running, hard. I have seen a leopard walk within about twelve metres of a motionless bushbuck. In more open environments, it pays to give early warning of a predator and to keep it in sight, for as long as the prey can see the threat it poses little danger to them. It is not uncommon to see a herd of impalas, snorting furiously, following a leopard or a lion at a prudent distance. The same methods are seen in zebras and wildebeests. Herbivores seem, moreover, to recognise categories of danger as

ABOVE "... before being lodged in the highest branches."

will scatter in all directions, at great speed, invariably bouncing along in the rocking horse gait known as stotting. What advantage the latter may confer on the impalas is difficult to say, but the desire to put a lot of distance between them and wild dogs is very evident. I was following a cheetah across fairly open terrain, approaching the Kapen river, when something about three metres ahead of us and six or so metres to the side of the cheetah caught my eye. It was a duiker, lying with its fore feet splayed out and pressed as close to the ground as was possible.

The situation was quite unlike what I would have expected had the predator been a lion or a leopard. Firstly, had one of these two species come as close to a duiker as the cheetah was to that one, I would expect it to give an alarm call and race off. Secondly, it was the closest approach by a vehicle that I ever saw tolerated by a duiker.

The circumstances suggested that the duiker was well aware of how poor its chances of escaping a cheetah in that area were, and consequently was taking every precaution in order to remain unseen, to the extent even of not moving when a vehicle came uncomfortably close. It was still lying motionless when, several minutes later, I backed away and drove round it in order to follow the cheetah, which by then was almost out of sight.

represented by different species of predators. Thus impalas will treat lions and leopards in the manner described above. Once these animals, which rely on a pounce or a short rush at their prey, have been detected, they abandon that particular hunt. However, when a pack of wild dogs, cursorial predators that run at their victims and catch them through persistence, endurance and numbers, comes into view, a herd of impalas

ABOVE Fastidious feeders, leopards are also meticulous in their attention to grooming.

PREVIOUS PAGES A half-eaten carcass is taken out of a tree and dragged into cover by the Trollip's crossing female.
ABOVE Animals with woolly fur are usually plucked extensively before feeding commences.
OPPOSITE When not feeding on a kill, leopards spend most of their time lying up near the base of the tree in which it is stored.

Feeding

The leopards that I have watched often, though by no means always, started by plucking the hair from the part of their prey that they started feeding on. This seems to be more common with particularly furry animals. Although I made no note of it at the time, I seem to remember that the woolly fur of duikers and scrub hares was more often plucked than was the smoother pelt of impalas. In performing this function, the hair is gripped between the upper and lower rows of the incisors and tugged out with quick upward and backward movements of the head, and discharged from the mouth through the flexible offices of the tongue, accompanied by much grimacing and expressions of evident distaste, which perhaps accounts for the desire to remove the stuff in the first place. Presumably, unduly woolly fur makes for uncomfortable eating and swallowing. In this regard one should recollect the reluctance of some lions and one leopard to eat baboons, and the distaste shown by one lioness that did.

Since both these predators, and in particular leopards, will feed off a variety of species including carcasses in the final stages of decay, an aversion to the flesh might appear unusual. Besides being coarse and fibrous, baboon hair is singularly resistant to plucking. Kim and Dale noticed that male leopards were more inclined to pluck carcasses than were females. In the Kalahari, plucking was found to have occurred in six out of thirty kills. These six carcasses were of carnivores and antelope young; animals with relatively woolly hair.

With medium and large sized prey, the hindquarters are invariably eaten first. The skin is peeled back and where possible ignored. All the bones of a manageable size are consumed, which in an impala includes most of them, except for the vertebrae and pelvic girdle. Most of the skull is eaten but parts of the jawbone and the teeth customarily remain. The legs of an impala lamb may be devoured in their entirety, down to the hooves. The viscera are eaten with the exception of the stomach contents as well as those of the gut.

Leopards, and lions as well, have the habit of sucking the intestine in through their incisors, thereby expelling the contents. In the latter stages of consumption, a carcass may consist of several scraps attached to one another by tenuous connections of skin and sinew. Although they become very adept at securing their kills in sometimes very precarious

ABOVE "With medium and large sized prey, the hind quarters are invariably consumed first."

lodgings, leopards seem quite oblivious to the effects of gravity and I have often seen a piece of the carcass, at times a substantial one, fall to the hyaenas waiting below when the strip of skin holding it together was chewed through. A more comprehensive account of the feeding process is to be found in Bailey.

The rate of consumption seems to be fairly standard for different individuals. A leopard is seldom found at a kill for more than two consecutive days before it is finished. The one notable exception was the West Street female, who had a remarkably small appetite, and stayed with a female bushbuck she had killed for five days and with a six-month old impala for four. Leopards tend to lie close to their kills, usually on the ground for the sake of comfort, but sometimes on a branch of the tree wherein the kill has been stored. They may leave the area to drink

but do not appear to do this to any great extent. In my experience it was extremely uncommon to find a leopard that was lying up with a kill anywhere but in the immediate vicinity, although these observations did not include the time between nine o'clock at night and six the following morning, this being the part of the day we customarily reserved for eating and sleeping.

I mention this for the sake of factual accuracy, though it does not seem likely that leopards would use this time to do anything other than eat and rest. Feeding is mostly conducted at night, especially when the days are hot. As a general rule, visiting a leopard with a kill during the day is a fairly certain guarantee of observing some prime inactivity, while arriving at the same spot at sunset is usually rewarded by the leopard feeding within a few hours.

ABOVE "The legs of an impala lamb may be consumed in their entirety, down to the hooves."

ABOVE Mlowathi male and warthog. Warthogs have tough skins which may require time and effort to peel back.

Interactions with other Species

O f all the other species that a leopard
may encounter, the most dangerous is
the lion and it is accordingly given the greatest
respect and, where possible, the widest berth.
The usual reaction of a leopard meeting up with
lions is to climb high into a tree and, if the lions
approach closer, to go higher still should it
be possible. Thus secure, a leopard may
occasionally be forced to spend long periods
of time at the leisure of its life-long foes
gathered below.

ABOVE The Flockfield male warns off a hyaena approaching his kill.

CHAPTER EIGHT

ABOVE The Mlawathi male keeps a careful eye on a pride of lions some distance off in the bed of the Sand river.

Lions

I have seen a young male leopard, between two and three years old, spend an entire day, and a very hot one too, in the thin and uncomfortable upper branches of a knobthorn tree. The reason for this was that four lions had chosen to sleep in the shade of the selfsame tree, having chased him up it early in the morning. Another young male also spent a day up a tree although the lions, in his case, were lying up about seventy metres away. It was a cool overcast day, however, and a more comfortable tree and the leopard was also much younger, about a year old and still with his mother. He watched the lions intently most of the time that he was up the tree, not inclined to take the slightest risk even if the lions were too far away and, for most of the time, fast asleep. This has a parallel in the behaviour seen in prey animals such as impalas; so long as they can see the threat, they are safe. Turnbull-Kemp describes a similar situation during a beat that was being conducted in India in a small patch of brush that contained, not only the tiger that was being beaten for, but a leopard. The leopard repeatedly climbed trees, not in order to elude the beaters – as will be seen later, the opposite approach is usually taken where humans are concerned – but that it might be constantly aware of the exact position of the tiger, as both animals were moved around. A typical encounter took place between a two year old female leopard and a pride of lions one evening. Whether the leopard

was in a tree when she saw the lions, or climbed it after detecting them I do not know. When I arrived she was lying along a branch some four metres off the ground, watching the lions with absolute concentration as they approached. She did not move until they were close to the base of the tree, and then climbed as high as she could into the smallest

ABOVE Unlike leopards, lions hunt almost exclusively at night.

branches, remaining there until the lions were well gone. I suspect that, where a leopard has sufficient warning, it would prefer to slip quietly away from lions and put some distance between it and them, rather than climb a tree where it is then effectively trapped.

In an encounter between the Mlowathi male and the Charleston pride, however, he chose the latter option. The Charleston pride had arrived at a waterhole in the morning. They had killed an impala earlier in the day and one of the cubs was carrying, like a trophy, a bone from one of its legs. Having drunk, they lay up on the northern bank. That afternoon we followed the Mlowathi male into the same area, where he threw himself down on a patch of sand to roll. Suddenly he shot upright and gazed intently to the north for ten or so seconds before dropping to the ground and slinking off in a southerly direction. The bank was steep and undercut here and as it was more than likely that he had seen the lions, I expected him to disappear once he had gained the summit and was out of their sight. However, once I had manoeuvred round, he was found lying on the branch of a tree that was growing out of the bank, watching the lions, who were now approaching the river bed, very carefully. One of the cubs was in the lead, craning her neck as she looked ahead; the rest of the pride was following lethargically. Evidently the lead cub had seen the leopard and, not recognising clearly what she was looking at, moved slowly closer. The pride, perceiving her interest, followed. They walked past where the leopard had been lying and slowly moved out of sight in an upstream direction.

Once they had passed, the leopard slipped down the tree and walked away in the opposite direction. Although the tree was not a very high one and its branches were quite stout, which would have permitted a lion to have climbed fairly high into it, the leopard was seemingly of the opinion that it was more advisable to watch the lions and be certain of their intent and direction before moving himself. That is assuming that it was indeed a considered action.

I believe that leopards are certainly capable of assessing a situation and treating it on merit. In contrast to the usual reaction of climbing high into a tree and maintaining a wary vigilance, is the Airstrip female's encounter with the Emsagwen pride one night. She bumped into them in the middle of a large open area known as Piccadilly triangle, where suitable trees were few and far between. She climbed up a dead leadwood that was only about thirty centimetres in

diametre at its base and no more than seven metres high. The lions did not appear to notice her, or if they did, ignored her, and strode on at a good rate. Sometimes lions can be very lethargic and disinterested when hunting and at others much more intense. This was one of the latter occasions and the leopard seemed to recognise it, for they were scarcely fifty metres away when she came down the tree in a graceful series of elegant slides and hops and jogged off in the opposite direction, without once looking back.

I would have considered her actions as somewhat risky, with lions close by and in an open area, but she was in no doubt at all. True, she

ABOVE The fearsome nature of a lion's talons is evident from this unsuccessful attempt to get at a leopard's kill.

ABOVE "The leopard had seen the lions coming and took refuge up a small, shrubby bush-willow."

wasted no time in moving on, but then she seldom did so anyway when active at night. 'Time is protein' might have been her motto. The Mlowathi male had a kill taken from him by the Styx pride, that he had stored high in a tree. The young female of the Styx pride was then half grown and with a little effort managed to scramble up the tree and steal the carcass. While she was doing this, the Mlowathi male – who had climbed higher into the tree when the lions arrived – slunk lower, and dealt her a buffet that caused her to tumble partway down the tree. It is inconceivable to me that he, or any other leopard, would have taken such liberties with an adult lioness.

In the event of a leopard being caught by a lion, it is practically defenceless. The same young male that spent an uncomfortable day up a knobthorn was, a few months later, caught and mauled by the Charleston pride. They surprised him at close quarters and gave chase, clawing him out of a tree that he tried to climb. The pride was then three subadults with their mother; the subadult male was the most ferocious, standing above the leopard long after the others had left it and savaging it at the slightest movement. Eventually the lions left and the leopard limped off, sorely wounded. He was not seen again and it is likely that he died from the punishment he had taken. Several cubs were killed by lions over the years. One of the Matshapiri female's cubs was caught by the Emsagwen pride but neither killed nor, apparently, even harmed, in an incident with inconsistencies on both sides. The leopard was a female, two years and two months old; the lions were also young,

two surviving lionesses from an originally larger pride. The leopard had seen the lions coming and took refuge up a small shrubby bush-willow. Inexplicably, when the lions came closer, the leopard jumped out of the tree and was caught running off.

The only explanation that I can think of is that she felt insecure in the small tree. The lions quickly caught her; equally inexplicably, she was not mauled and escaped to climb another tree like the first. It was at this point that I arrived at the sighting, having heard of events up to now in summary over the radio. The leopard spent no more than a minute up this second tree when without warning she jumped down, ran off again and again was caught. What surprised me was the speed at which she was running, for leopards can move like a whiplash when there is need; she was almost gambolling along, uttering short explosive growls as the lions gained on her. In the summer vegetation it was not possible to say what happened when she was caught, but a few seconds thereafter she was away again and climbed a third tree. This time she stayed put. It can happen that a leopard which feels threatened by a person or a vehicle will leave the safety of a tree, but in this case she was an habituated animal. Long after the lions had left she was still up the tree and quite unconcerned with the vehicles.

It was some time after the lions had departed that the leopard's mother arrived. Ghostlike, she was suddenly noticed on top of a termite mound, staring ahead with intensity and, presumably, concern. She may have recognised her offspring's growls or suspected the worst when she heard the noise. Possibly, she merely heard lions and investigated. She was taking no chances and crept forward very slowly, pausing for long minutes and looking ahead. Eventually she found her cub, and neither before nor after they met up did either of them make any sound. The cub descended and moved briskly off to the south. The mother, eventually, went east.

The fact that the lions did not cause any hurt to the leopard is unusual, especially since they were nearly full grown and she was much smaller. Where the size and strength differential is less, an animal may understandably be reluctant to grapple with an enemy. Adult hyaenas, for instance, were chased and sometimes caught by lionesses but never, in any instance that I know of in this area, mauled. Perhaps the lionesses' youth and inexperience were, in this incident, explanation enough.

Seventeen months later the Emsagwen pride, consisting then of one of the original lionesses and a newcomer, caught and killed a leopard cub that was about six to eight months old. The Hogvaal female came to a sad end a day after she had caught a steenbok. The kill was dragged into the Matshapiri river but not taken up a tree; here, in the sand, she was found the next day.

Perhaps she had been surprised while sleeping, for lions can move very quietly. Lying amongst a wealth of lion spoor, her body had been bitten about the neck and the lower back. Her hindquarters were

dislocated in the lower spinal area and were completely twisted around. While on the topic, it is worth looking at the effect that humans have on leopards since it can have unpleasant consequences on their interactions with lions. A leopard will not stay up a tree if a human approaches on foot. In the case of an animal that is not habituated to being viewed, the same applies to a vehicle. Perhaps they are in some way aware that humans can climb.

Baboons certainly seem to be aware of this. If one approaches a tree with baboons in it, they descend in haste and run away, which would be suicidal behaviour were it applied to lions. Whatever the reasons, it is a fact of leopard behaviour. It is probably safe to say that it is an invariable one. Usually a nervous leopard would hardly ever, if at all, allow a vehicle anywhere near it. However, should such an individual seek refuge up a tree from lions, it might be seen by humans who must then be very careful indeed, since approaching too close to the tree may cause it to jump out.

Such a situation was described by Jonathan Scott as having happened in the Masai Mara, when vehicles crowded too close to a leopard that had been treed by lions, with fatal consequences for the leopard. Unless the leopard's identity and behaviour are known, great caution should be employed and the animals viewed from a substantial distance, or left alone.

ABOVE Lions sometimes suffocate larger prey with a clamp hold on the muzzle, a technique not yet recorded in leopard.

Hyaenas

Of its competitors, the hyaena is the greatest pest from a leopard's point of view but statistically probably hardly ever a serious threat to it. In the southern part of the reserve where hyaenas were more abundant, seldom did a large kill go undetected by them. Sometimes they followed leopards when they were hunting and often appeared on the scene of a kill within minutes or less of it having been made.

When a kill up a tree was discovered, the hyaenas invariably camped out below it to seize the scraps that fell. Sometimes a reasonable amount of food might be secured in this fashion, especially if young leopards were involved. Hyaenas in the Sabi Sand probably rely mainly on scavenged or stolen food, unlike the situation in plains systems like the Serengeti or in Savuti, where they live in large clans and chase down prey on a regular basis. They are consequently not likely to be severely handicapped by injuries. One female that we knew for at least two years had lost one of her back feet but was always in prime condition and even reared cubs.

Leopards, however, can ill afford any form of incapacity and are therefore less likely to risk injury over so inconsequential an issue as food. In a direct confrontation with a hyaena, a leopard will invariably relinquish a carcass. There are exceptions, however. The Jakkalsdraai male was on several occasions seen to have left a kill on the ground, when it could easily have been taken up a tree, and defend it against up to three hyaenas. He used his claws against them, slashing out with his head well out of reach of their jaws, and eventually lost all but one kill

that I can bring to mind. This one had been dragged to the summit of a termite mound, from which position it was more easily protected. The KC male chased off hyaenas that were hanging around a kill that he was sharing with another leopard. I saw a young male leopard that had made a kill and was feeding off it on the ground when a single subadult hyaena arrived. The leopard snarled at it and for a few minutes it kept away, but then slowly drew closer and started feeding, ignoring the leopard's warning growls. Eventually it was tucking in with gusto, tugging and ripping at the carcass and finally the leopard gave up and walked off.

The Hogvaal male's kudu kill was shared between him and a hyaena. There was no need in this case to squabble over it owing to the quantity of available food which took them both over three days to finish, feeding separately and resting for hours between meals. I have always wondered, however, whether that hyaena perhaps deliberately made no fuss over the leopard in order to avoid competition from its own kind.

In this area hyaenas tend to forage singly or in small groups of two and at most three. I have, however, witnessed several incidents illustrating how a single hyaena or a small group, arriving at a lion kill, may call in reinforcements with their whoops and giggles. The response to these calls was quick and not infrequently, provided enough hyaenas arrived and the lions were few in number, they managed to drive off the lions and appropriate the kill. Perhaps the hyaena that discovered the Hogvaal male kept very quiet, not wishing to draw the attention of its fellows to the carcass and thereby losing a few days worth of feeding. It is

ABOVE Hyaenas often cool off during the day in the summer months, a habit shared with tigers but not the African cats.
OPPOSITE Wistful patience generally provides a small yield for hyaenas where adult leopards, such as the Flockfield male shown here, are concerned.

a tempting scenario to imagine but hard to say how close it is to being correct. Predators certainly appear to be possessed of an elementary cunning. I have seen a lioness catch an impala and race off into the darkness with it, returning empty-handed to the rest of the pride before a male, who had been trailing behind, had caught up to them. He had heard something and sniffed around with great interest but the females, lolling around, grooming each other and playing with the cubs, were giving nothing away. There are also the two occasions when the Chellahanga female, joined by the Jakkalsdraai male while she was leading her cubs to a kill, deviated from her route in order to shake him off. Such an explanation is not necessary in the case of our hyaena, however, who faced with a single leopard, had no need of any support. Still, there is perhaps a small possibility that it tolerated the leopard and did not engage in any form of conflict for fear of broadcasting the presence of so much food.

Kills sometimes changed hands several times. The Chellahanga female was found with the carcass of an adult male impala which was on the ground, perhaps owing to a lack of suitable trees. A hyaena moved in and fed off it and then retired, whereupon she reclaimed it. During an hour it passed back and forth three times in this way. Eventually the leopard dragged it to the base of a tree. She inspected the trunk for a long time, repeatedly picking up the carcass and then letting it fall. The tree was straight and tall but had a thorn branch pressed close to the trunk about two metres off the ground. It would have been an awkward obstacle to have passed with an impala in her jaws and was, I suspect, the reason she did not make the attempt. The carcass was left on the ground and by the next morning was gone, taken by hyaenas.

It was with the greatest interest that I read of a male leopard in Bailey's study who went by the title of M23. This remarkable animal caught and ate at least three hyaenas, probably while they were investigating his kills. Bailey saw him approaching a kill that he had temporarily left, and stalking and chasing a hyaena, this time unsuccessfully. From a photograph of this leopard, he appears to have been of average size and not exceptionally large as might in a way be expected of an animal with such audacious habits. Apart from showing how bold leopards can be, the unusual practices of this individual also provides an indication of their adaptability and catholic taste in foods. The greatest threat posed by hyaenas, is certainly to the cubs; as has been seen in chapter three, this does not seem to be statistically very significant. In this area, well provided with trees to climb and adequate rocky den sites, a cub should only suffer death by hyaena as a consequence of ill fortune or poor motherhood. In conclusion comes the most unusual leopard and hyaena interaction, also starring a warthog, which I have left until last. The Sparta female, toward the end of her days, caught an enormous male impala which she dragged to the base of a tree that was growing out of a termite mound. The evidence suggested that the kill had been made in the mid morning and during the day the carcass, which was too heavy for her to take up the tree, was fed off by her and by her well-grown cub. In the night it was, inevitably, discovered by hyaenas. She stood her ground for a while, perhaps reluctant, in her waning strength, to abandon such a valuable prize, before fleeing with

LEFT The disproportionately large neck muscles may enable hyaenas to spirit large and heavy parts of a carcass away from their competitors.

Complex Interactions

Interactions between species are rarely seen and are usually very brief affairs. Sometimes, however, events may pack a good deal of excitement into a short space of time, as the following two examples show. The Jakkalsdraai male was being followed late one afternoon. In the early evening, he encountered and was chased by a group of young male lions. Evading them, he soon thereafter caught a ten month old impala, and just as quickly lost it to some hyaenas, who chased him off. Later he caught and ate a scrub hare. After this he succeeded in catching an adult female impala, which was prudently taken up a tree. It was his misfortune, however, that evening, to suffer a further visit by lions. This time the young and small-bodied females of the River Rocks pride, drove him off and stole his kill. The Hogvaal female caught a duiker one morning and took it up a tree. It was still alive and the bleating attracted the Styx pride, lying not more than fifty metres off. They were unable to climb the tree, however, and after they had left the leopard took the kill down and dragged it into a donga, where in the afternoon an unknown leopard was seen feeding off it. The Hogvaal female, meanwhile, had moved off to look for her cub. On the way she was chased by a troop of baboons and ran for about three hundred metres from them before arriving in the area where her cub had been left. When she found the cub, it had been treed by a pack of wild dogs. The young leopard was quite unconcerned about the dogs, and when they had left she came down the tree. On the way toward her mother,

ABOVE Mutual grooming is commonly found amongst social predators such as the spotted hyaena.

ABOVE Blackbacked jackals den underground, often in burrows in deserted termite mounds.

the hyaenas in close pursuit. As she ran past a second termite mound a young warthog stuck its head out of a burrow and, scarcely breaking stride, she snatched it up and ran to the nearest tree. But the pursuit was too close, and the loss of time occasioned by the pig's weight was crucial, and a hyaena seized her by the hindquarters as she jumped into the tree. The warthog was promptly released, flying back over her shoulder and barely touching the ground before it was grasped by a hyaena.

who was sitting on a termite mound some distance off, she retrieved a steenbok kill from under a bush and took it up a tree. The following morning, both of the leopards were found at the duiker kill. That afternoon only the cub was found, stalking zebras and kudus (the only instance I know of where a young female leopard showed interest in such large prey), and the morning after that she was back at the steenbok, of which, by this time, precious little was left.

ABOVE The Toulon female (left) and her son watch some hyenas that chased them off a kill.

Jackals

Jackals are not infrequently seen at lion kills in this area but never at those of leopards. To a lion, jackals seem insignificant. Hyaenas, if sufficiently plentiful, may drive a lion from its kill, and vultures, while incapable of any direct threat, perform an unwelcome service by advertising the presence of food to other predators. Both are greatly disliked by lions and are chased and, circumstances permitting, killed. Jackals, however, fall into neither category and are largely ignored by lions. They flit around the outskirts of kills, darting in to claim the scraps. I have even watched while one rather intrepid animal sneaked quietly between two lions while the pride was contesting a kill to snatch a mouthful and retire undetected. They are, however, conspicuously absent at a leopard's kills and with very good reason too, for to a leopard a jackal is not so much an irritating presence as a welcome meal. I think it possible that in this area, jackals do not as a rule raise the alarm when a leopard is sighted. I base this on the fact that I have only twice known them to do so, and there must have been many more times, in the hours that I have spent following leopards, that they were seen by jackals. On both occasions, the jackals were probably responding to the leopard because of their pups. In the one case, a pair of jackals that was known to have pups bayed at a leopard that was walking across the open area

that they were commonly seen in. The other was more definite; the Airstrip female caught an impala virtually on top of a termite mound wherein dwelt a litter of young jackal pups. I do not think the leopard was ever aware of how close she was to them, but their mother certainly was and she set up a continual howling at a distance of about ten metres from the leopard. Logically, it would appear sensible from a jackal's point of view not to draw a leopard's attention to itself under normal circumstances.

Cheetahs

The wooded vegetation of the Sabi Sand does not favour cheetahs greatly and their numbers are low and appearances sporadic. A month or more may go by without any cheetah sightings, though this is unusual, sometimes they might be seen two or three days in a row. Contacts between them and leopards in this area are consequently very infrequently seen. Physical interactions between the two species are probably highly unusual. A leopard would have little difficulty in causing severe injury to a cheetah, which in turn, equipped with weaker jaws and doglike claws adapted to running rather than grasping and slashing, is unsuited to returning the compliment.

ABOVE *Cheetahs eat quickly and quietly, always alert to the arrival of stronger predators.*

A cheetah is therefore well advised to avoid any physical contact with a leopard and this, owing to a running ability beyond that of any other land animal, they are more than capable of doing. I do not know of a single case in the Sabi Sand where a cheetah came to grips with a leopard. They have, however, been recorded as prey items of the latter animal in other areas. Leopards were seen chasing cheetahs off their kills on two occasions. In each case the leopard was a female but the sex of the cheetahs could not be determined. A young female leopard was found staring at a cheetah across a dry pan. After about ten minutes she went after the cheetah, which eluded her with ease. The Flockfield male walked past a cheetah, which watched him from a distance of thirty or forty metres. Neither showed any particular interest in the other.

Wild Dogs

In accordance with what appears to be a general rule amongst predators, wild dogs will show aggression to and mob, where possible, any other predator. I have seen them growling and rushing at lions on a few occasions, and running from them too when the lions became annoyed and chased them. In turn they chase leopards, who easily evade them by climbing trees. On at least three occasions, we have found leopards, or rather had them found for us, while following dogs. The dogs move at a rapid trot and if one can stay with them, there is often some action to be seen. Usually this is in the form of a kill for they have a high success rate of attempted hunts, charging at their prey in numbers and at high speed. I suspect that this apparently inflexible habit, well suited to plains systems but which they do not appear to adapt even in the thickest bush that occurs on Mala Mala, is responsible for many of the injuries that they are frequently seen carrying, especially the pups, and may in part account for their low numbers in the KNP.

The rapid progress that they make through the bush, and the way in which they are usually spread out while so doing, means that they cover a lot of ground and this is how leopards may be found while one is following dogs. In the instances that we observed, the leopards climbed trees and stayed in them showing little excitement, climbing down when the dogs had left, which did not take long. I bumped into a pack of dogs lying on the road one morning. They are seldom inactive for very long unless the day is hot and they have fed – for them there are two speeds – fast forward and stop. So within ten minutes we were bowling along at a merry pace, following the dogs as they trotted down the road. It was during one of the Chellahanga female's consortships with the Jakkalsdraai male, and we had seen them mating over the previous three days. Halfway along an open area the dogs stopped and looked into the ground to the side of the road, then bounced through the grass with

tree within easy access, is anyone's guess. I have no predictions as to the outcome. Wild dogs are themselves potential prey; jackals are not infrequently taken as are domestic dogs. Usually the numbers of a pack are sufficient defence but as one might expect, a leopard is quick to seize an advantage as happened in the following incident, described to me by Lex Hes. A female leopard had caught and killed an impala. While she was feeding on the carcass, which had not been taken up a tree, a pack of dogs consisting of two adults and a pup arrived on the scene, chased the leopard away and took the carcass. Later a different leopard, also a female, happened upon them. Arriving unnoticed, she stalked and caught the pup, and quickly hoisted it up a tree.

ABOVE An opportunistic dash and pounce lifted this wild dog pup from the security of its pack.

their ears pricked forward, rising up on their hind legs and uttering little growly barks. They had detected the two leopards who, as the dogs got closer, climbed into a small Combretum. The dogs milled around the base of the tree for about a minute before moving on, whereupon the leopards came down and promptly mated. What might happen should a leopard be taken unawares by a pack of dogs, surrounded and with no

Other Small Predators

As mentioned earlier, little tolerance generally exists between predators of different species, presumably for reasons of competition. A pride of lions, for instance, will maintain a territory against other prides since to tolerate them in the same area is to suffer

ABOVE It is estimated that wild dogs are successful in about eighty percent of the chases that they initiate.

the loss of prey animals. In certain areas where prey is generally or seasonally scarce, this could have serious consequences. Leopards, cheetahs and hyaenas, however, also feed to a large extent on the same animals as do lions and are therefore an unwelcome source of competition. In the case of the leopards' relations with other predators, the situation is slightly different since, owing to the breadth of their dietary spectrum, many smaller predators constitute not only competition but prey. Mongooses, civets, genets and wild cats have all been caught and consumed. Recently I saw the Chellahanga female kill a civet which was left untouched. This is not necessarily a case of eliminating the competition, but could well be a simple chasing response. Once the animal was caught, the urge to eat it may have been absent. Honey badgers are paradoxical creatures, often very shy, sometimes pugnaciously bold. Lions have been known to give way to them and even on occasion

ABOVE Despite the functional aspect of its nose, the snouted night adder is not a burrower.

surrender kills. Following the Charleston pride one evening, just after the sun had gone down, I watched as one of the females inched round the side of a termite mound in order to look at something that she had probably heard. She stopped, then cautiously backed off and walked on, giving the spot a wide berth. Driving round to the other side of the mound, I was amused to find a honey badger grubbing around in the dust. Conversely, the Styx pride was found one morning playing with a dead honey badger that they had presumably killed some time earlier.

Smaller than lions and self-reliant too, leopards should be expected to follow the example of the Charleston pride. It was surprising therefore

to read Bailey's account of a struggle between a honey badger and a leopard that tried to catch it. In the ensuing fracas, the honey badger lost the back of its scalp and the leopard sustained deep wounds on its chest and legs. A honey badger's skin encloses its body in a voluminous fashion and is loosely attached, enabling it to twist around and bite whatever happens to grab it. The only time that we recorded a meeting between these predators happened when the Newington female and her two cubs encountered a honey badger. All three leopards tried to climb the same tree, but only the mother succeeded, and the cubs were chased by the honey badger and were last seen disappearing in the direction of the

ABOVE A drying pan preserves a civet's nocturnal ramblings.

river. One might as well include vultures in this section. Perhaps leopards regard them in much the same light as do lions, but the way in which their kills are hidden in trees or under cover means that they are hardly ever discovered by the vultures and so I have never seen any interactions between the two. A curious observation of John Hunter's reads as follows:

"During the day, the bait would be so covered by vultures that nothing could be seen but a wriggling mass of black feathers and scrawny necks. Sometimes a hyaena would take a flying leap on top of this tangle and break a hole through by the mere weight of his body. We often saw leopards feeding beside the vultures. I have noticed that when leopards have finished, they will often grab one of the vultures and carry it off with them – I suppose as desert."

He was writing of a hunting safari that he took into the Ngorongoro crater sometime just after 1910. It was the first such safari in that refuge; the crater had been barely visited and Hunter retained the services of a guide to take them to it. The observation is as interesting for the suggestion that leopards were then regularly to be seen scavenging at large carcasses on the plain as it is for their treatment of vultures.

Snakes

Most animals seem to have an instinctive fear of, or at least respect for snakes. I saw very few interactions between leopards and serpents, and only one involving cubs. The leopards in this case were about five months old and had been left near a large termite mound that had some vegetation covering it as well as a tree growing out of the apex.

They had discovered or been discovered by a puff adder crawling around on the mound and they showed a bit of interest in it and certainly a fair amount of respect. They did not approach closer than about one metre from it. A year or two earlier, I had been following the Hogvaal male when he found a puff adder. He was much more concerned with it, following gingerly as it slowly crawled under a rock, hissing from time to time and once jumping back, I presume at a quick movement on its part. This happened at night and in long grass so it was not easy initially to see the snake. A bit later, when it crawled up a slope and into plain view, the leopard stood back, watching it intently and with great interest. A young adult male leopard was walking down the main access road,

ABOVE The serval's large and forward-oriented ears enable it to pinpoint its prey by sound alone.

marking regularly. He was new to the area. Frequently, he would leave the road and walk a short distance into the grass in order to sniff at and spray a nearby tree. He had just started on a Combretum when he reared up on his hind legs and retreated, without any particular haste, and walked back onto and down the road.

The most likely cause for his behaviour that I could think of was a snake, and being curious to find out if this was the case and yet no more enthusiastic to get to grips with it than the leopard had been, I drove cautiously forward.

As I slowly approached the spot, a medium sized black mamba rose out of the grass and glided up the tree. Walking as quietly and as extensively as they do, leopards must encounter snakes reasonably often during the course of a year and run some risk of being bitten, especially by puff adders that have a habit of lying still and reacting only when stepped upon. They account for the majority of snake bites that are inflicted upon humans out of doors. I think that the remarkably quick reflexes of leopards are probably of sterling service in this regard. I was watching the Mlowathi male sleepily, according to appearances anyway, walking along a road

ABOVE Curiosity and apprehension; the Hogvaal male and a puff adder.
BELOW RIGHT Pythons are a potential threat to small cubs.
OPPOSITE The viciously barbed slender three-hook thorn offers no resistance to elephants' gullets.

Large herbivores

The interactions of buffaloes and rhinos with young male leopards have already been described. In general, leopards seem to ignore animals that are beyond their ambitions of catching – namely elephants and giraffes – and this attitude, on the part of the animals concerned, appears to be reciprocated. This is unlike the disposition of the same animals in so far as lions are concerned, the difference being, obviously, that lions are a threat to the young of both species. Elephants always demonstrate when they see lions, in my experience, and mostly chase them as well. Encounters and interactions between leopards and elephants were not common. A female leopard sat watching two elephants that were fighting in the river, evidently with some interest. The only encounter that I saw happened when the Hogvaal male met an elephant in Buffalo pans. He was skirting a dense fringe of gwarri bushes and to have continued along that line would have meant passing within less than ten metres of the elephant, which he decided to do, at a run. The elephant spun round as the leopard ran past him, then followed after with his head up in a position of mild threat. The leopard, once he was past the elephant, slowed down and stalked away at a stroll. Thus dignity seemed to have been preserved on both sides, the elephant seeing the leopard off, who in his turn affected indifference to the larger animal. Giraffes do tend to show a little more concern with leopards, though not much. I have seen giraffes watching leopards carefully for as long as they were in view. They did not, however, seem to show the same concentration as they might have had it been a lion that they were observing. From a lion, of course, there is an element of risk to themselves as well as to their young, whereas a leopard presumably is only a threat to a young giraffe, and a very young one at that, under unusual circumstances. Although small giraffes are recorded as leopard prey it is uncommonly so. By contrast, it is estimated that between 50% and 75% of giraffe calves are taken by lions and hyaenas before they are a year old.

when he suddenly and instantaneously whipped his body over in some species of back somersault, that was too quick and unexpected for me to have been sure of what had happened. Nor, scrutinising the spot after he had moved on, could I find anything that might have accounted for his reaction. Scorpion, serpent or sharp piece of gravel approximating the same, whatever it was that had seized his attention, it was evident that his responses were equal to the occasion. Snakes are in any event not often seen in the area. The only animal we knew of that might have been killed by one was a cheetah that was found on the point of death, frothing at the jaws. An autopsy performed at the KNP was unable to offer any positive cause of death, but the veterinarians considered that snakebite was a likely explanation.

Mortality

In a conversation with Lex Hes, both of us totalled up the number of cubs that had survived to independence out of all those that we knew to have been born, and each arrived at a figure of exactly 50%. This would seem therefore to be a fairly accurate approximation of the actual average for cub survival.

Of the cubs that do not survive, violence or misadventure is probably the primary cause of death rather than disease. I say this because I cannot think of a single cub that was seen to be ailing before it died.

RIGHT Young female leopard at sunset.

CHAPTER NINE

Cubs and Subadults

However, Bailey found that leopards could lose condition very quickly. An adult could go from perfect health to a state of emaciation within a month. Therefore a cub, especially a very small one, might sicken and die within a much shorter period, and if the leopards were not seen during this time its illness would go unremarked. One cub that did succumb to illness was recorded; its mother had mange and both died as a result.

Lions are probably the greatest single cause of cub mortality. Only three cubs were recorded as having died of known causes; one died from the mange, the other two were killed by lions. Hyaenas are certainly a threat, but in this area, as earlier detailed, they are probably not a significant source of fatalities. The one case where they were a factor, taking into account the cubs reported by Lex Hes, as left in a termite mound, could perhaps be attributed to carelessness on the part of the mother. Sundry predators may also be a factor, particularly when the cubs are very small and still in their initial den site. The Airstrip female's first cubs disappeared after about a month with no clue as to what had become of them. There was no evidence to suggest that they had ever been moved from their first den, which appeared to have been a very good one, within the rocks at the top of an overgrown koppie about ten metres high; certainly a good choice with regard to lions or hyaenas. Months after the loss of her cubs, while passing by the same koppie, I saw a honey badger running up it. Not enough is known about these animals to even be able to determine whether they are territorial or not; if they are, however, or even habitual in their movements, then the choice of a koppie that may have been regularly used by one of these aggressive little animals, as a refuge for her cubs, would have been an unfortunate choice on the part of a leopardess.

Bailey recorded a similar case where a leopard kept her cubs in a reedbed, not four metres from a hole wherein resided a python at least three and a half metres in length. Twenty-two days later, the leopard stopped using the reedbed and her subsequent movement patterns and association with a male suggested that she had lost her cubs. The python, which was twice seen by Bailey in the same position in the reedbed during the leopard's absence, must figure as a prime suspect. The rocky, overgrown places that are selected by leopards with small cubs are also likely to be used by smaller predators, especially pythons. This type of predation is therefore perhaps a constant though not significant cause of cub mortality. Out of at least forty-four births recorded by Bailey, Hes and myself, predation of this nature was indicated in only two cases. Its effect on the population is further reduced when one considers how quickly a leopard can recycle after losing small cubs.

Bailey recorded fifteen adult and subadult leopard deaths. Nine were as a result of starvation, two were owing to natural violence, one came about from poaching activity and in three of the cases no cause could be found. Starvation was therefore by far the greatest cause of mortality, particularly amongst females and more especially where subadults were concerned. Of the seven subadult deaths, five occurred through starvation and the other two could not be attributed to any cause. Four of the five that starved were females. Before examining these figures and how they tie in with the data that was collected, it is necessary to look at another cause, or effect, of loss of condition and

ABOVE A young male leopard takes no chances with a pride of lions sleeping about seventy metres away.
OPPOSITE Leopards frequently use lookouts in unfamiliar territory.

ultimately death in leopards. This is mange, which in leopards is caused by the skin parasite *Notoedres cati*. Animals manifesting this condition suffer hair loss which in turn may lead to increased pigmentation, accounting for their dark appearance. The skin becomes crusted and cracked and eventually secondary infection may set in. The question that begs itself is, which is consequent upon the other: do leopards that contract mange lose condition, or does a loss of condition lead to mange? In other words, is mange a primary affliction in its own right or merely a symptom of general debilitation? A detailed investigation of this issue is to be found in Bailey.

It appears, however, that mange is probably a consequence of poor condition and not a cause of the same. It seems likely that most individuals carry a small number of the parasites, which only erupt into epidemic proportions when the host is stressed or malnourished. A large proportion of the subadults that starved, four out of five, were females. One could think of two reasons for this state of affairs; firstly, that they were inexperienced or inept at hunting, and secondly that they were excluded from prime areas – or indeed from any area at all – by territorial females, and lost condition as a result. Based on our records and observations, I believe that the first condition probably applies. Here some of the issues that have been described in previous chapters can be considered. First is the fact that leopards are not taught to hunt but learn on their own, starting as cubs with small prey. In connection with this is

the individual differences that cubs from the same litter display, some being bolder and more alert while others are nervous and hesitant, appearing 'backward', if such a term can be applied, when compared with their sibling or with other cubs. These individuals may not be capable of surviving when cast onto their own resources. The situation takes a further dimension when the following quotation from Bailey is considered :

"Animals often become susceptible to mange if deficient in vitamin A. Felids have a high vitamin A requirement and must obtain all their vitamin A from prey (Scott 1968). But vitamin A is restricted to specific tissues, mainly the liver, and also the lungs, adrenals and kidneys. Body fat and muscle tissues are virtually devoid of this vitamin. If certain leopards survived on a diet of small prey, or scavenged remains from larger prey for prolonged periods, they could have become vitamin A deficient. The internal organs of small prey probably do not provide the same amount of vitamin A as the liver or other organs of impala-size prey. Scavenged skin and bones would provide little, if any, vitamin A."

Thus a subadult female that is unable to make the progression from catching the small animals that she started on as a cub, to capturing larger animals, specifically antelopes, could lose condition firstly from obtaining an inadequate quantity of food, and secondly from a vitamin deficiency that would further render her susceptible to mange.

This theory also ties in with the observed differences between the behaviour of male and female cubs and subadults. The males were far bolder and showed a greater willingness to tackle larger prey; the Mlowathi and Hogvaal males caught an adult warthog and kudu respectively, while they were still subadults. Thus they would be less likely to suffer from emaciation and vitamin deficiencies. Of the single subadult male that he recorded as dying from starvation, Bailey wrote that the only kill he made after he became emaciated was a civet, and that he had never been known to kill an impala even before he lost condition. This observation fits in fairly well with the theory that I have postulated. The faeces of two emaciated female leopards that Bailey collected contained vegetation, small mammal remains and parts of an impala that suggested, from their composition (hooves, bones and hide) that they had been scavenged. The second possible reason for subadult females to have starved – that they were excluded by territorial females – would not, I believe, account for their emaciation. Here we can consider the case of the West Street female. For as long as we knew her, she was chased from territory to territory; by her sister from the area to the east of their mother's range, then by the Hogvaal female from hers. Thereafter she went south, and there too, judging by the subsequent wounds that she bore, ran into difficulties of tenure. Yet never was her condition anything less than very good, from the standpoint of a visual assessment. She caught adult

ABOVE The West Street female was chased from one territory to the next, and soon vanished entirely.

ABOVE "A nine month old female asleep in a knobthorn tree."

antelopes and even a subadult baboon, which indicates that she was not lacking in enterprise and daring. What, then, was her ultimate fate?

This is a question that can be posed for a number of animals in an identical situation. The Hogvaal female's first two cubs, as well as her next, the Hogvaal male, the Sparta and Trollip's Crossing males and the KK Crossing female as well as several others were all born to relaxed mothers and grew up with and were completely at ease with vehicles, which would have made them easy to follow through adolescence and adulthood; all abruptly vanished at varying times after reaching independence. None were ailing before they disappeared. Some of these individuals may have moved out of our area as well as that of neighbouring reserves, from where reports of their future might, and in some cases did, come. However, such migration could not entirely account for this phenomenon, especially where individuals like the West Street female and Hogvaal male are concerned. Their ranges were situated well within the reserve – certainly in the case of the Hogvaal male – and one day our records of them simply terminated. The logical explanation is that something violent befell them, and though it could well have involved another species, the one factor that more successful subadults, who grew from cubs born to known females into territorial adults, had in common, mitigates against this. The Flockfield and Mlowathi males, and the Chellahanga and Airstrip females all grew to

maturity within areas that were not known to be occupied by adult leopards. No lethal fights between adult and subadult animals were seen, but instances of great savageness were, and the evidence of other encounters was present in the form of wounds and scars. The carcasses of two male leopards were found, which may have been killed by other leopards. So although no direct evidence of leopards killing other leopards prevailed, there is good cause to suppose that it was a factor, especially in the case of subadult animals that were unable to find unoccupied ranges.

Adults

A number of diseases and parasites have been described that might affect leopards. Only one case of an apparently healthy animal succumbing to sickness was known in the time that I was in the area, and this was a young adult female that died of mange, along with her cub. At least three other leopards were seen suffering from this disease; two were subadults and one a nervous adult male. One of the subadults, a female, died. Her death was reported to us by rangers from a neighbouring reserve; the exact cause was not determined but in light of the preceding section, a combination of malnutrition and mange seems

ABOVE The Hogvaal male; another leopard who lived to be successfully independent, and suddenly disappeared.

to have been most likely. The other two, both males, were not seen more than twice. Bailey's study showed that adults could survive the disease, and this means that their demise can not be presumed, at least in the case of the adult. This makes the case of the young female leopard something of an anomaly with regard to the general situation for mange, as it appears to exist. Perhaps she contracted the disease, or simply a

more virulent infestation of the mites, in the same fashion as might any of the adults that Bailey had recorded. Although we did not notice any changes in the condition of established adult leopards, our means of assessment were based on their visual appearance. Bailey, however, recorded seasonal fluctuations, most of his leopards losing weight in the late wet and early dry months. It could have been during such a period

by lions. Three other adults – the Marthly, Kapen and Airstrip females – disappeared without trace. All were young adults and none were showing any signs of weakness before vanishing. The most likely agency for their demise is lions. Hyaenas are potentially a threat but although encounters between them and leopards were commonplace, I did not see any approach a life-threatening situation, or even one where there was much risk of injury for a leopard. Nor did the leopards take them particularly seriously.

How easily could a leopard be taken unawares by a lion? They are generally so quiet and good at evading danger – in areas where they are not habituated to people they may almost never be seen – that to be overpowered in such a manner may seem unlikely. Lions, however, are not without their own facilities of stealth and I saw at least two instances where, by chance, they came very close to a leopard before the latter animal detected them and took rapid evasive measures. Over the years, a number of potentially serious encounters of this nature must be experienced by a leopard. The Sparta female was injured by lions in the last few months of her existence and the Chellahanga female had a narrow escape, seen by Kim and Dale, which left her enfeebled for some weeks after. Even a shy and alert animal must sleep, however lightly, and although dozing leopards are usually responsive to noises that are out of the ordinary, perhaps even they forget themselves in depths of slumber and are thereby vulnerable to attack from a predator that, approaching unheard, comes upon them. In support of this idea I will relate a tale concerning the Mlowathi male, which happened when he was a young animal slightly over two years of age. The incident took place during the time that he was habitually spending his days resting up at Flockfield Boma Crossing. He had been sleeping next to a backwater for several hours when a family of pigs trotted down to take the waters, some time around midday. They did not see the young leopard quietly dozing in the shade of a clump of reeds, and drank several metres from where he lay, savouring the cool water with a characteristic amount of lip-smacking and sotto voce grunts. Despite the noise, which was not excessive but clearly audible, the leopard did not stir, and only when the warthogs had finished and were trotting off did he lift his head to gaze blearily in their direction. "So that's what it was", his expression seemed to say, "I thought I heard something". And, laying his head once more on his paws, he fell asleep again.

Do leopards dream? I am not well informed on the subject of animal's sleep patterns and perhaps there is no way that we will ever know the answer to this question, but I have seen a female leopard, who fell asleep while we were watching her, fall into deep, regular breathing and begin twitching and kicking with her back legs very much like a dog in front of a fireplace.

Leopards can suffer injury when tackling their prey. They have been recorded as having been killed by bushbucks and by baboons. Porcupines are an occupational hazard if preyed upon and lions are not uncommonly found severely perforated by their quills. These, being equipped with microscopic barbs, resist being pulled out and can lead to infection and incapacitation, sometimes resulting in death or in the afflicted animal resorting in extremity of hunger to feeding on humans. Leopards have elsewhere been found with quills lodged in their bodies, but in this area porcupines were not even recorded as prey items during the period of study. Just after writing this, I have been advised that the

of reduced condition that the female suffered from an increased number of the parasitic mites. Unlike the leopards in Bailey's study, however, she did not recover.

Natural violence may be the most common cause of death in adult leopards, the males perhaps more so than the females. Only one of our habituated adults died from a known cause; the Hogvaal female, killed

Jakkalsdraai male was found with quills sticking out of him, but not to any serious degree. It has also been reported to me by Chris Daphne that there was a population explosion recorded among porcupines during 1997. During the years that I worked in the area they were pretty uncommon; a month or more might have gone by without one having seen so much as a single animal. This low density alone was probably reason enough for their having been so little recorded as prey. A leopard's cautious approach when hunting would probably prevent it from taking overt risks with porcupines. Even youngsters seem to show a healthy respect for them. I watched the Flockfield male running after a porcupine when he was about two years old. The grassland had been burnt and he trotted after it, behind by a metre or two as it scurried along. After a few minutes he either became impatient or thought that he had seen an opening, and rushed at the porcupine. There was a loud squawk and the young leopard backed off, shaking his head. He had sustained no visible damage in the process. The West Street female, at three years of age, studiously avoided a porcupine that came her way but the Hogvaal subadult, when she was twenty-three months old, was involved in a twenty minute interaction with a porcupine, which she followed but refrained from tackling. Stevenson-Hamilton had the following observations to make on the subject:

"Leopards with porcupine quills sticking in their feet and bodies are occasionally brought to bag, but never, in my experience, present the pitiable spectacle of emaciation so frequently noticed as lions in similar cases. Perhaps their method of hunting, consisting, as it does so largely, of lying quietly in wait for their prey handicaps them less when thus temporarily crippled. Something too they may owe to their great natural cunning and activity, which enables them to elude the sharp spines, which form the porcupine's sole, but far from contemptible method of defence."

I have not encountered any reports of a leopard having been killed by a warthog, but at least one lion, a male, is on record as having suffered this fate. A vein in his neck was severed by a fortuitous – from the warthog's perspective – slash. Judging from our records and observations, injury from prey animals is a negligible source of fatalities to leopards. For reasons earlier discussed, the less risk averse males are probably more susceptible to becoming casualties of this particular mishap. In the absence of concrete evidence of how adult leopards meet with misadventure, we can perhaps look at their own assessment of the threats that they face; an application of the old saying that actions speak louder than words. By their hasty evasive actions and the exaggerated caution that leopards display toward lions – quite in contrast to the cool and offhand fashion in which hyaenas are treated – they tell us that here is one of their more significant perils. The only leopards whose cause of death could be established during the study – two cubs and an adult female – were killed by lions.

Two of the male leopards in Bailey's study were eaten by crocodiles; the one caught by a crocodile, and the other probably caught too and not merely scavenged. Owing to the ease with which male leopards take

ABOVE The West Street female looking over the territory that she hunts in, but cannot hold.
OPPOSITE Leopards are not as active during periods of full moon, when the light favours their prey.

ABOVE Like leopards, lions almost invariably use a stranglehold to kill their prey.

to water, compared with females, these large reptiles may constitute an occupational hazard in areas with permanent rivers where their numbers are high. The Sand river, being temporary in nature, supports neither large numbers nor sizes of crocodiles. In this area therefore they are of negligible concern; in others they may be a significant source of fatalities.

The threat that an adult leopard constitutes towards another adult seems to be minimal. The long-term boundaries that adult females maintain suggests that they avoid conflict with one another; the various interactions between adult males indicate that disputes are often concluded without resorting to violence. The Flockfield male yielding up a large part of his range to the Jakkalsdraai male, and the latter animal giving ground to the Mlowathi male are examples. In settling these disputes animals may eventually resort to physical means, as was seen between the Chellahanga and Trollip's Crossing females, and as can be deduced by the scars that frequently embellish the faces of males. It would appear, however, that these fights are seldom pursued to a fatal conclusion. The one piece of evidence suggesting otherwise is that of the Trollip's male, found dead in the river bed, apparently a victim of a violent encounter. What evidence could be discerned did not, in the opinion of Gavin Hulett who found the carcass, point towards lions. In the absence of any more definite indications as to the nature of conflicts between adult animals, it appears that the majority of serious conflicts probably take place between established adults and encroaching

subadults. In these encounters the greater size and experience of the adult would be an advantage, and could therefore lead to the older animal initiating a fight. This is particularly true of males, which may take up to five years – based on observations on the Mlowathi and Flockfield males – to achieve their ultimate size. A youngster of between one and a half and two years would be at a great weight disadvantage, and would also probably be lacking in aggression too. If this process is a factor, it could explain why so many subadult animals suddenly disappeared from sight.

The same handicap would not apply to females to such an extent; some adults are quite small and more of a size of a robust subadult. The Hogvaal female, it must be remembered, appeared to come out second best in her fight with the young White Cloth female. In a study in Israel, the results of which are presented by Bailey, Giora Ilaney documented several instances of violence between leopards. A younger female fought with an older female and expelled her from a substantial part of her range. It was also believed that a younger male leopard had expelled and possibly killed an old male. Old age probably accounts for a significant proportion of adult animal deaths, particularly females. Four individuals at least certainly lived out the maximum span that an animal can be expected to achieve under natural conditions. The Sparta, Matshapiri, Trollip's Crossing and Island Crossing females were all of aged and venerable aspect toward the end of their days. The Sparta female and the Trollip's Crossing female were both still with their last litter when the latter were at an advanced age, long past the time that their mothers would normally have kicked them out. The Sparta female was still with her son when he was twenty months old, and of all the females whose maternal activities were recorded, she had the briefest associations with each litter. The Trollip's Crossing female remained with her final set of cubs until they were twenty-two months old. Both females lost condition rapidly in the last few months of their recorded careers. A similar situation pertained to the Matshapiri and Island Crossing females although they were less frequently observed. The Island Crossing female was nervous and inhabited, moreover, fairly impenetrable terrain. The Matshapiri female, although relaxed, lived in an area less frequently covered by us and not well supplied with roads. When she was last seen, her advanced age was very evident; the occasion was, in fact, the time that one of her cubs was caught by the Emsagwen pride, discussed earlier in this chapter. Her cubs were then two years and two months old. Her condition, the age of the cubs that were still with her and the fact that she was not seen again indicate that she was with her last litter.

All of the radio-tagged female leopards whose deaths were recorded by Bailey died from starvation, while only 25% of the adult males and 33% of the subadult males succumbed to this cause.

To what extent might a male leopard be expected to live to the utter limits of his muscle and sinews, and perish finally from the accumulation of time? Misadventure is probably more likely to overtake him than it would a female as his lifestyle is less reliant on caution and might set a shorter limit to his days. If, however, he is not caught by lion or crocodile, and does not suffer impalement from the tusks or horns or quills of an animal that manages to turn the tables on him, there is no apparent reason for him not to enjoy the same protracted span of years that females are capable of achieving. Consider the following examples, collected by Turnbull-Kemp, of individual males to whom a minimum term of existence could be assigned:

"... four redoubtable Eastern Leopard man-eaters started their careers as adult animals – and were well-known for seven, eight and nine years before being destroyed. None of these beasts could have been less than three years old when its career as a man-eater started – since all were known to be have been adult at the time – and thus none can have been less than ten, eleven and twelve years old when trapped or shot. Only one was described as showing signs of age on death. Dunbar Brander writes of a black leopard which had been known 'for years', and records having seen this in 1913, subsequently seeing the same animal in 1923. This writer fails to mention having noted any obvious signs of age in this extremely well-known and distinctive Leopard ten years after first seeing the beast. In 1946 I was shown the mutilated spoor of a male Leopard which had escaped from a trap in 1935, the creature being well-known and described as 'big past all' at the time when it was trapped eleven years previously. ... Colleagues of mine who have remained stationed in one place for many years inform me of clear-cut cases where adult leopards – usually males – have been easily identified and clearly resident at one point for periods of up to sixteen years. The latter instance points to a minimum age of not less than nineteen years."

ABOVE Free water is not critical to a leopard's survival; they can reportedly sustain themselves on the fluids of their prey alone for up to two years.

The Flockfield male, when last seen, was exactly eleven years old and showing no signs of decrepitude or stress. Since his territory moved steadily south and is now effectively beyond the bounds of the area that we cover, and we have lost touch with him, it may well be that he has many years yet left to him. As was seen in his interactions with the Jakkalsdraai male, a dominant animal's career is by no means over should he be edged out of his territory by another leopard. Kim and Dale saw the Flockfield male mating with at least three different females within his range in the KNP, showing that he was dominant in that area. The Jakkalsdraai male is still, at the time of writing, in the prime of his life. If he continues as successfully as he has done to date, he may provide us with valuable information on a leopard's longevity.

Infanticide

Male lions are known to kill cubs that are not their own and this has been extensively documented. In Mala Mala, this happened on at least five occasions while I was working there. With leopards, the situation is far less well known. There was evidence that it occurred twice in our area. The first inkling to be found was largely circumstantial and happened after the Jakkalsdraai male had moved into a large part of the Flockfield male's range in the south. Before his arrival, the Chellahanga female had been seen with the Flockfield male in October 1991. No mating activity was observed, but in June 1992 she was seen with a cub, estimated then to have been about four months old. Since his range overlapped hers at the time and he was seen mating with other females in the area, it is very likely that he had sired the cub. In any event, it is certain that the Jakkalsdraai male was not the father. The cub was last seen on 12th August 1992. The Jakkalsdraai male was first seen in the area in September 1992. On the 21st of the same month, he was mating with the Chellahanga female and on 9 February the following year, she was seen with new cubs. The exact date that the Jakkalsdraai male first encountered the Chellahanga female may have been earlier than that on which he was first seen in the area, and although the cub was last seen before our records indicated that the male moved in, sightings of the Chellahanga female were not common during this period. The cub may therefore still have been around by the time that the male met up with its mother, and although the evidence is purely circumstantial, there is a strong suggestion that the Chellahanga female's cub was killed by the newcomer male, who then mated with her. This female had a high success rate. She raised all the cubs that she was known to have delivered, with the exception of the one under discussion, to independence, so the demise of the one at the same time that the Jakkalsdraai male moved in would seem to be owing to more than coincidence.

ABOVE In the winter months many herbivores, and hence the predators that feed on them, concentrate around the Sand river.

The Flockfield male moved south, and from that time on the Jakkalsdraai male controlled all the matings that were seen to have occurred in the area that he had taken over. In June 1994, the Flockfield male was found carrying a dead cub in his jaws; he was being followed by the Sandy Crossing female, who three months previously had been seen lactating. There was no reason therefore to suspect that the cub was anyone else's but hers, and as the Jakkalsdraai male had been seen with her eight months prior to this event and because he was the dominant male in the area, there is every likelihood that he was the father. There is of course the possibility that the cub had not been killed by the Flockfield male. Presumably there would be no other reason for him to have been found carrying the dead cub, with its mother following anxiously some twenty metres behind. However, females whose cubs have died invariably end up eating them. It is not unreasonable therefore to suppose that a male, chancing upon a female with a dead cub, might not seize it and carry it off, and quite possibly consume it. This possibility cannot therefore be ruled out, although again I feel that there was more to the issue than simple coincidence, where a male leopard was found carrying the carcass of a cub that he in all probability had not begot. Dealing with the scraps of evidence in this issue is a frustrating exercise. Although the picture hovers in front of us, showing how a newly dominant male will kill existing cubs and sire his own, the conclusive evidence is tantalisingly elusive. From Ilaney's study in Israel, however, comes a wealth of concrete evidence.

"At least three different male leopards killed a minimum of eleven leopard cubs during a nine-year period (1981-89) (Ilaney 1990). One male (Ben Aflul) killed an eight-month-old male cub and immediately bred with its mother (Humbaba), who gave birth to his offspring one year later. Another male (Ktushion) killed two cubs of another female (Shlomtsion), then bred with her to produce a male cub that survived. Ktushion also killed two cubs of the other female (Humbaba) in 1983. She, however, bred with the other male (Ben Aflul). Humbaba and Ben Aflul produced a male cub that survived. A seven-month-old male cub of the female

ABOVE Yet lithe and slender, this male will be in his prime in about two years.

Shlomtsion was also killed by the adult male (Ktushion), as were three of her other cubs. Another adult male leopard (Hordos), son of female Shlomtsion and male Ktushion, killed two three-month-old cubs that were born to his own mother from her mating with another male (Amrafel). One female (Humbaba) was not able to successfully rear a cub since 1983 because all her cubs were killed by male leopards. All the male leopards in this small population competed for the right to father their offspring with one female (Shlomtsion). Not a single adult leopard was added to this population from 1984 to 1989 primarily because of cub mortality from infanticide (Ilany 1990)." Quoted from Bailey, 1993.

Ilany's study was conducted on an isolated population and illuminates the danger of restricting animals to increasingly smaller tracts of land. As a side issue to that of infanticide, it shows how reluctant adult males may be to fight one another, rather tolerating a rival than putting oneself at risk through combat. Clearly the area they occupied was overstocked, with disastrous consequences for the population's breeding success, yet no single male was sufficiently able, or willing, to completely evict a rival from his range. Consider then why this phenomenon, so well known in lions, has only recently come to light in the case of leopards. This is, I believe, owing to two reasons. The first is the shyness of the species which makes such observations difficult. Even in the area where I watched them, which had a large population of completely habituated animals, much of what they did remained unseen. Lions, however, are as a species far more visible and flamboyant, and tend to draw attention to themselves during such exciting events that, in the case of leopards, would go unnoticed except that one happened to be watching them at the time or arrived on the scene fortuitously. In one of the instances wherein we recorded infanticide in lions, our notice was drawn to the area by the noise that was being generated and on approaching closer, lions were to be seen running in many directions, with much vocalising. In another, the fight took place during the small hours of the morning and the participants rampaged through the camp, waking almost every occupant in the process and, following up on their tracks the next day, the body of one of the cubs was found.

Secondly, the tenure of dominant male leopards is far longer than that of lions, which affords a greater stability to their range. Male lions are seldom in control of an area for more than two years; when a new coalition takes over, small cubs are immediately at risk. A male leopard, on the other hand, may remain dominant within his territory for a far longer period. Consider the examples listed by Turnbull-Kemp, as well as that of the Jakkalsdraai male, who has been in the same range, controlling all the observed matings therein, for five years and at the time that this was being written was still pre-eminent. From the time that he moved in, therefore, his area has enjoyed stability with no serious challenges that we have detected. The killing that was possibly, or probably, perpetrated by the Flockfield male took place on the border of the Jakkalsdraai male's range, in an area that was used and marked by the former animal. For the reason first given, infanticide in leopards would be rarely seen; for the second, however, it is apparent that in a population residing under natural conditions and under no stress of limited area, it probably does not happen very frequently.

RIGHT The leopard with the greatest character as I perceived it, and my favourite, was the Airstrip female.

Just Leopards

I would dearly like to have known the weights of the individual animals that I was familiar with. This basic piece of information has been subjected to much exaggeration and falsification over the years. Hunters like to have shot big animals, and all manner of wildly inaccurate claims for their sizes, as well as improbable aspects of their behaviour, have over time crept into the literature. Field guides sometimes give very general, and occasionally incorrect, information in this regard, and even reliable studies are themselves of little use in estimating the size of a specific animal in the field.

ABOVE The Hogvaal male at two years of age.

CHAPTER TEN

ABOVE Female leopards are smaller in the head and forequarters than males, and appear to have a proportionately longer tail.

Male leopards, for instance, average about sixty kilograms in the Kruger Park region. The heaviest recorded by Bailey was seventy kilograms, and the maximum weight that a leopard in any area may attain seems to be in the order of ninety kilograms, or two hundred pounds. What, then, did the Mlowathi male, and the Flockfield male weigh? Were they of average size, or larger? For some reason, this particular statistic held a great fascination for me, and occupied a fair amount of my idle thinking time. Small facets of behaviour, what amounted almost to idiosynchrasies of the species, and other trifling theories and observations also came to hold my attention, and together with the more mainstream issues of ecology and natural history, build a picture of what I understand a leopard to be. This chapter deals in a loose fashion with some historical items, observations and lines of reasoning that I found interesting.

Names

What is a leopard? The size and colour of the animal varies greatly within a population, so that throughout its range, as well as through time, people have tended to split it into two and sometimes three supposedly different species. The Romans claimed to recognise at least two different animals. Building on their records and on the writings of early naturalists, which often had more in common with mythology than they did with natural history, the early authorities had by the Middle Ages listed three different species – the pard, the panther, and the leopard.

When sportsmen of the British Empire actually came into contact with these animals, the confused situation was given impetus by the fact that the natives of Africa and India themselves recognised two different types of leopards, which they categorised on the basis of size. In the Transvaal, for instance, Stevenson-Hamilton reported in 1940 that the locals separated the leopard of the low-lying bush, which they referred to as 'm'balana' (the small-spotted) from the animal that lived in the hills to the west, which was said to be larger and lighter in colour, with longer hair and bigger spots which they knew as 'Indzimba'.

In India, reference was made to village panthers, which were small and lighter in colour than the larger, darker forest-dwelling animal, which had a thicker coat and was known as a 'thendu'. An exceptionally large animal was also called a gol bagh - literally, 'spot tiger'. The village panthers were said to live on offal and small animals that they caught or scavenged on the outskirts of settlements, so that the variation between the two types were sometimes attributed to differences in environment and diet.

In Africa, folk lore has associated differences in temperament with size differences. Turnbull-Kemp has this to say on the matter:

"Both native and European hunters will commonly claim that the smaller Leopards of any given country are more savage than the large examples found in the same region. Strangely, although I have only a few dozen cases which I have been able to investigate, this seems to have some truth in it. Nevertheless, I think that the main cause is that small Leopards are those most often found in the immediate vicinity of human settlement, and it is these with which man most often comes into contact. There is the additional possibility that the most determined attacks from Leopards on man may come from female animals. Lyell, an experienced hunter in what used to be called Nyasaland, was one of the writers who recorded this belief, stating that the Africans considered smaller 'hill' Leopards to be far more ferocious than the bigger Leopards of the plains of that country. This leads one to a different but very common misconception. It is not safe to be too dogmatic about 'hill' Leopards being consistently smaller than those from lowlands, for the great gaunt beasts so typical of many lowland areas also occur in the hills and mountains – leaving aside for the moment the really heavy and powerful forest animal."

One wonders also what a 'hill' leopard really is, according to these hunters' perceptions. Certainly within an extensive mountainous area, such as the Drakensberg or in parts of the Cape Province, animals may spend all or the majority of their time in such terrain and, as will soon be seen, this type of habitat seems to result in a smaller size of leopard. It does not seem likely, however, that a hill habitat of so all-encompassing a nature would have been encountered by the hunters and locals who fuelled the early theories. One imagines rather that they referred, in at least some of the cases, to koppies and small hills, in areas where the average range of a leopard would cover these outcroppings as well as the surrounding plains. As was discussed in chapter two, such hillocks do not seem to be particularly favoured by leopards, although they may well be used as daytime refuges in areas of high human densities, especially where they are hunted. They are, however, highly regarded as den sites by females with small cubs. Anyone encountering a leopardess on or in the immediate vicinity of a koppie wherein resided her cubs would very possibly leave with an earnest belief that small, hill-dwelling leopards were much more aggressive than the larger ones that were to be found on the plains. With respect to the village panthers that have been described in India, I suspect that not a few of them could very well have been immature animals, forced out of better forest habitat by established adults.

ABOVE The Flockfield male as a young adult; note the differences with the female opposite.

The proportions of the tail were one factor that was initially used to separate the two types of leopards that Mediaeval writings and native beliefs had created. By the mid-1800's, scientists had established that Africa was inhabited only by panthers, while India had both panthers and leopards. It was only around the turn of the century that it was recognised that what had been classified as two distinct animals represented, in fact, the extremes of a large range of sizes and colours. For whatever reason, the all black animals that sometimes occur owing to melanism are invariably known as black panthers rather than as black leopards, so that nowadays it is often believed that the difference between a leopard and a panther lies in the fact that the latter animal is black.

ABOVE The Flockfield male in his prime, showing the thick neck of a mature adult.

Perhaps this is because in India, where examples of melanism are more commonly encountered than in Africa, leopards were often known as panthers. Maybe it is simply because the name rolls off the tongue in a more pleasing fashion when the word panther is used, and has thereby fallen into more general use. Although the melanistic specimens are sometimes described as being all black, the spots are in fact slightly darker than the ground colour, from which they can be distinguished in favourable light. In South Africa, the situation was further confused by the fact that early settlers were in the habit of referring to leopards as tigers. Today, a leopard is still often known as a 'tier' in rural areas, especially in parts of the Cape Province, and not necessarily incorrectly so either. Animals frequently acquire local names, and this is one with a long history of common usage behind it. Whether he was aware of the tenuous grounding of these arguments, or, as is more likely, that he was simply poking fun at people as was his wont, Herman Charles Bosman has provided us with as good a last word on the debate as any, in his short story "In the Withaak's Shade".

"Leopards? - Oom Schalk Lourens said – Oh, yes, there are two varieties on this side of the Limpopo. The chief difference between them is that the one kind of leopard has got a few more spots on it than the other kind. But when you meet a leopard in the veld, unexpectedly, you seldom trouble to count his spots to find out what kind he belongs to. That is unnecessary. Because, whatever kind of leopard it is that you come across in this way, you only do one kind of running. And that is the fastest kind."

ABOVE In dense cover, curiosity can be critical to a leopard's survival.
ABOVE RIGHT Agile and supple, leopards are supremely at home in trees.

Concealment

One of the most characteristic features of a leopard is most evident when the animal itself is least so. This refers to its powers of concealment, which are considerable. The coat is strikingly marked, and I have had many comments from people who, looking at a photograph of a leopard, wonder how it can possibly hide itself when it seems to stand out from the landscape in such a prominent fashion. Photographs, however, are usually only taken in situations where the animal is displayed to best advantage. The leopard crouching low, pressed to the ground in mottled shade, is often unseen, and when it is, seldom photographed. I wonder how many times I have looked at leopards under these types of conditions without seeing them. There are many accounts of leopards which have suddenly resolved themselves before an onlooker. Kingdon writes of how his first sighting of a leopard suddenly jumped into view when he realised that he was looking at its eyes. A similar thing happened to a friend of Turnbull-Kemp's, waiting alongside a firebreak in a patch of bush that was being beaten for a leopard. He noticed a cloud of midges drifting along the track and only when it had come close enough for him to see the slitted eyes in the midst of the insects did he realise that he had been watching the leopard. When the Hogvaal male was about a year old and still with his mother, she killed a juvenile impala which kept them busy for a day. Arriving at the appropriate tree the following afternoon, I found no immediate sign of any leopards nor at first of the kill, which was soon seen lying in a crumpled heap at the very base of the tree. From a viewing point of view

ABOVE On occasion I've felt that leopards choose the most difficult way of doing things in trees, just to show that they can.

it had to be established how much meat was left on the carcass, from which might then be assessed whether the leopards would return to it. Although leopards usually lie close to a kill, they do sometimes leave it, perhaps to drink. In this case we had to know what the likelihood of the animals returning that evening might be, otherwise time could be wasted by returning to a spot which they had abandoned. The carcass was not easily visible from the vehicle and a closer examination would be necessary. Although no leopards were apparently in the vicinity, I knew from experience that they are often closer than one imagines, so we submitted the area to a thorough visual search. After all of us had scanned around, my tracker and I stood up and looked again. Apart from providing a better view, this action will often cause a predator to reveal itself, as discussed in the first chapter. After all these precautions,

I slid out of the vehicle seat in order to approach and examine the carcass, and with that the young male leopard, who had been lying in the grass not six metres away, sprang up and moved off.

This incident illustrates another habit which leopards have, of not moving from where they are hidden until the last possible moment. They will tolerate a very close approach, at least of humans, and seem to judge a situation to a nicety. There is a well-known account of a leopard which was being monitored by a radio tracking device in Nepal, whose transmitter one day showed that it had spent the entire day in a village. Presumably it had entered the village at night in order to scavenge; finding itself trapped in the village come morning, it spent the rest of the day in a woodpile, scant metres from where the inhabitants of the settlement must have regularly passed. Hunting stories are full of like

ABOVE Cubs spend a great deal of their time in trees, seemingly for pleasure alone.
OPPOSITE This young male will spend less time aloft as he grows heavier and less frivolous.

incidents, which include wounded animals. The leopard is invariably far closer than it might have been imagined to have been, and several stories tell of maulings received from animals that jumped up virtually at the spot where they had been wounded.

In one case at least, the ground had been thoroughly worked by a party of men after a leopard had been shot, and only when the shooter retraced his steps, and stood exactly where it had last been seen, did it rise up and inflict grave injuries on him. He had just about stepped on it, the animal having sat tight while members of the follow up party had moved about within metres of where it lay. A leopard which is in the process of being accustomed to vehicles, and therefore is neither so nervous that it avoids them entirely, nor yet quite comfortable with them at a reasonable viewing distance will often, on being followed, crouch down in a suitable piece of vegetation. When it disappears, it is usually assumed that it has moved on ahead so that people following it pick up the pace and search likely spots to the front. However, if one retraces its steps and examines possible areas of concealment along the route it was taking, it is often to be found lying low, having let the vehicles pass it at sometimes very close range.

Speed

The same hunter's stories throw some light on the speed of reflex and of action that is another feature of the leopard. Tales of leopards that appeared in the twinkling of an eye, mauled several people

and escaped before any of the party had time to think of inflicting hurt on it in return are by no means uncommon. The accounts are numerous; here is a sample of what Stevenson-Hamilton, first warden of the Kruger National Park, had to say in this respect :

"Wolhuter, who shot one almost at his feet, said that the two points which specifically remained fixed in his memory were the pace the beast came at, and its insignificance as a target. A sportsman who recently was badly injured by a leopard in East Africa, remarked that his sensation was as though a glorified tennis ball was coming at him, and so rapid was the onslaught that he had not even time to pull the trigger before the beast was on him."

Although it concerns a distasteful subject, the following quote of Turnbull-Kemp's on the subject of gin-traps shows how phenomenally quick a leopard can be.

"It is rare", he wrote, "for a Leopard to be taken high in the foot, since its reactions are so fast that a trapped foot is partly withdrawn before the trap's savage teeth have time in which to clash together. Here has been the cause of many accidents to trappers, since the Leopard or Panther may be taken by a single toe, or a shred of skin."

Nowadays one is far less likely to experience the privilege – a dubious one in former times, if reflection is made on the conditions under which it was obtained – of witnessing at first hand this rapidity of motion that a leopard can exercise at will.

Under natural conditions, an animal will only occasionally, and under circumstances of stress, have cause to behave in so urgent a manner. I count it as one of the missed opportunities that over many

years of watching them, not once did I observe what I came to regard as the fabled speed of the leopard. Perhaps, I saw it happen every day. When photographing animals in motion, one becomes used to timing the picture, swinging with the movement and tripping the shutter at the right moment.

With leopards, this is very difficult to achieve. They climb trees and descend them, encumbered with prey or not, with a fluid grace that appears easy and unrushed but in fact is quicker than it looks.

During the years, I often found that I had missed the right moment and even after years of practice was never quite certain that I had caught it. Photographing leopards under these circumstances is rather a matter of shooting before it feels right, and generally, once it has been practised a little, this seems to work.

There were also the few incidents that have already been described of the Hogvaal female standing up to the hyaenas, the Mlowathi male's somersault, which happened too quickly to be exactly certain what had transpired.

Wayne Hinde saw the Hogvaal female in a hurry when a pride of lions approached a tree which contained her and a kill she had made. As she saw the lions she grasped the carcass in her mouth, and the next instant was at the top of the tree.

Never, Wayne told me shortly thereafter, had he seen anything move so quickly.

ABOVE *The thickness of a male leopards neck and the fat deposits round it are shown to good effect here by the Flockfield male.*

Leopard versus Human

Quite a popular topic of conversation in wildlife circles concerns itself with which animal it is preferable to be beaten up by; a lion or a leopard. I have often heard it expressed that a leopard is the worse option, the reason given that they are used to dealing with baboons and therefore have no difficulty in adapting to humans. As has been seen, however, baboons are by no means a regular prey item. Nor does either predator's method of capturing its prey have, under normal circumstances, anything to do with the maulings that it delivers upon humans. Humans are feared by the large cats and given a wide berth. Most attacks on us are perpetrated by wounded or cornered animals, usually the former. The assault is therefore invariably a desperate act born of fear. A mauling from a lion is greatly to be avoided, and the main reason for this is simply the size of the animal. Any adult lion is much bigger than an average human male, while most leopards are smaller, especially the females. Judging from accounts written on the subject, anyone who does not perish from a lion's attack can probably consider himself fortunate. They use their jaws, which are large and very strong, to good effect. Bones may be broken and survivors are not uncommonly incapacitated as a result of these encounters. Leopards on the other hand seem mainly to use their claws. The teeth may be anchored in the shoulder, and at least one person has been scalped by the talons of a forepaw which were

ABOVE *The Airstrip female had the greatest affinity for trees of any leopard that I followed.*

ABOVE Leopards feed singly and in turn, lions compete vigorously and noisily, each striving to wrest the largest possible amount from the others.

sunk into the skin at the back of the victim's head and ripped back. Meanwhile the back feet are working away in the region of the abdomen and upper thighs with commendable industry. The result does not usually appear to involve any major damage but requires a lot of suturing. In the days before antibiotics, such injuries would most likely have resulted in death through septicaemia. Nowadays a mauling from a leopard seems unlikely to be fatal, although determined attacks can result in serious injury and even death. An incident related by Turnbull-Kemp is reminiscent of the old jokes concerning the sharpness of samurai swords and Ghurka kukris – where the assailee thought he had got off scot-free until invited to shake his head or blow his nose – and also shows how quick a leopard can be.

"The extreme sharpness of the claws of the Leopard's forefeet, unless it is an old or recently trapped example, coupled with the immense strength behind the slashing blows of the paws, has one startling traumatic effect. It is best illustrated by a tale told to me by an African Game Scout, with all the macabre enjoyment the African can get from such anecdotes. Briefly, the story was this. A Leopard charged into the midst of a group of Africans, lashing out with its paws. One of the men, struck on the thighs by the beast (which, by now, had vanished) was cackling with delight that the skelm had struck him but had done no damage. When he looked down again, he gave a wail of hysterical woe – parodied with delight by my informant. The deep cuts made by the claws had now sprung open and were welling out their blood."

Activity Patterns

Leopards are generally perceived as nocturnal animals, while lions are often regarded as more diurnal. In fact the situation, in natural populations, is almost exactly reversed. These perceptions have probably arisen from a combination of factors. Early film makers were restricted to working in daylight hours. This was perhaps owing to the difficulties of operating with separate light vehicles, but probably mainly to the rules of the National Parks in which they worked, which governed that vehicles had to be back in camp by sunset. Thus the earlier documentaries showed lions hunting during the day which, although it happens, is very minor in comparison with their nocturnal activities. With regard to leopards, animals that live in association with humans, such as on and around farming areas, quite possibly do become nocturnal, hiding from people by day and conducting their affairs at night. And within reserves and protected areas, leopards are initially more likely to be seen at night, by people driving, or specifically looking for animals with spotlights. This is owing to the greater confidence that an unhabituated leopard displays at night. For the same reason, occasional sightings of leopards are obtained in farming areas, in vehicle headlights at night. An impression is thereby formed of a nocturnal animal. In respect of this, it is interesting to note that Norton's studies of leopards' diet and movements in the western Cape showed considerable daytime activity. His animals were located on and around farms and rural areas, where they were effectively never seen and where good reason would exist for them to have become nocturnal.

However, the large numbers of rock hyraxes in their diet indicated that they were active during the day, since earlier studies had established that those prey species were, in that area, exclusively diurnal. This was then confirmed by monitoring their movements through radio tracking. In natural circumstances however, a leopard is possibly as active by day as it is by night. It would be intriguing indeed to know exactly how much of a leopard's time is spent sleeping. Not very much at all, I would imagine, the more so when compared with lions. As a general rule, and one which seems to apply to them almost unfailingly, lions hunt at night, and sleep by day. If they are found in the morning, there is every likelihood that they will be at the exact same spot that afternoon, still sleeping. Only as the sun begins to set do they become active, slowly and with many rests. By the time that it is properly dark they are hunting in earnest.

By contrast, a leopard that is found in the morning is almost guaranteed to be a long way distant come afternoon, sometimes to the tune of several kilometres, particularly if it is a male. I know of very few exceptions to this. One case that comes to mind is the Flockfield male, who was left lying under a bush at about 09h00 on a very hot day, and was still under the same bush at about 16h00 the same afternoon. The Airstrip female almost made a habit of proving the exception to the rule in this regard. On several occasions, all in summer, as far as I recall – she climbed a tree sometime in the morning, lay down on a comfortable branch and was found in the same position that afternoon. This was unusual not only for the fact that she spent the better part of the day in the same place, but that it was spent up a tree. She definitely had an affinity for them.

Day or night, leopards appear to sleep in short bursts, cat-naps in the literal sense, which are interspersed with periods of activity. Besides the case of the Airstrip female, these sleeping periods were, in my experience, of a few hours duration at the most. To what extent they sleep at night I do not know, nor am I aware of any studies that have examined this. Lions have two activity periods at night, one when the sun has gone down and the other early the following morning.

I have known leopards to take an hour or so off to sleep in the early evening. If they are lying with a kill, however, the majority of their time is devoted to sleeping. Leopards appear to call at much the same time as do lions; early in the evening, just after the sun has set, and again just before dawn. If one is fortunate enough to hear a leopard calling after sunset, close enough that it can be quickly investigated and found, it invariably turns out to be a male, marching along a road or game trail with a briskness of purpose and marking assiduously.

ABOVE Marula trees seem to be favoured perches, owing to the comfort of their large thornless boughs.
OPPOSITE Young leopards may take the risk of going down burrows after warthogs, and have even been known to succeed.
OVERLEAF Although play is often utilitarian in practising skills, it may simply occur for no reason other than enjoyment.

Bibliography

Specific Works

Bailey, T. 1993. *The African Leopard: Ecology and Behaviour of a Solitary Felid*. Columbia Univ. Press.

Hes, L. 1991. *The Leopards of Londolozi*. Struik Winchester.

Hinde, G. 1992. *Leopard*. Collins.

Scott, J. 1985. *The Leopard's Tale*. Elm Tree Books.

Taylor, W. and G. Hinde. 1994. *An African Experience*. Southern Books.

Turnbull-Kemp, P. 1967. *The Leopard*. Howard Timmins.

General Treatments

Bosman, P. and A. Hall-Martin. 1997. *The Cats of Africa*. Fernwood Press.

Estes, R. 1991. *The Behaviour Guide to African Mammals*. Univ. of California Press.

Kingdon, J. 1977. *East African Mammals: An Atlas of Evolution in Africa*. Vol. 3A. Academic Press.

Historical Accounts

Anderson, 1954. *Nine Man-Eaters and One Rogue*. George Allen & Unwin.

1961. *The Call of the Man-Eater*. George Allen & Unwin.

1967. *The Tiger Roars*. George Allen & Unwin.

1959. *The Black Panther of Sivanipalli*. George Allen & Unwin.

Carrington-Turner, J. 1959. *Man-Eaters and Memories*. Robert Hale Ltd. Corbett, J. *The Man-Eaters of Kumaon. The Temple Tiger and more Man-Eaters of Kumaon. The Man-Eating Leopard of Rudraprayag. Jungle Lore. My India*. [All of these have been reprinted many times, most often by Oxford Univ. Press]

Hunter, J. 1952. *Hunter*. Hamish Hamilton.

Stevenson-Hamilton, J. 1947. *Wild Life in South Africa*. Cassell & Co.

Scientific Publications and Magazine Articles

Bertram, B.C.R. 1982. Leopard Ecology as Studied by Radio Tracking. Symp. Zool. Soc. London. 49 : 341 - 352.

Bothma, J. du P. and E.A.N. le Riche. 1984. Aspects of the ecology and the behaviour of the leopard Panthera pardus in the Kalahari desert. Koedoe Supplement, 27 : 259 - 79.

Bothma, J. du P. and E.A.N. le Riche. 1986. Prey preference and hunting efficiency of the Kalahari desert leopard.

ABOVE Pygmy kingfisher, here caught roosting, but usually seen as a brilliant flash of colour over water bodies.

ABOVE Wild dogs at rest. They typically display two speeds only - stop and fast forward.

In S.D. Miller and D.D. Everett, eds., Cats of the World: Biology, Conservation and Management. pp. 389 - 414. Washington, D.C.: National Wildlife Federation.

Brain, C.K. 1981. *The Hunters or the Hunted? An Introduction to African Cave Taphonomy.* Univ. of Chicago Press.

Ewer, R. 1973. *The Carnivores.* Cornell Univ. Press.

Grobler, J.H. and V.J. Wilson. 1972. Food of the leopard *Panthera pardus* (Linn.) in the Rhodes Matopos National Park, Rhodesia, as determined by faecal analysis. Arnoldia 5(35) : 1 - 9.

Hamilton, P.H. 1986. Status of the leopard in Kenya, with reference to sub-Saharan Africa. In Cats of the World : Biology, Conservation and Management.

Le Roux, P.G. and J.D. Skinner. 1989. A note on the ecology of the leopard (*Panthera pardus Linnaeus*) in the Londolozi Game Reserve, South Africa. Afr.

J. Ecol., 27(20) : 167 - 71. Marsh, B. 1990. Hunting Leopards. Magnum magazine, May 1990 p. 57.

Mills, M.G.L. 1990. Kalahari Hyaenas – The Comparative Behavioural Ecology of Two Species. Unwin Hyman. Muckenhirn, N. and J.F. Eisenberg. 1973. Home Ranges and Predation of the Ceylon Leopard.

In Eaton, R.L. (ed.) The World's Cats. World Wildlife Safari. Norton, P.M. 1986. Ecology and conservation of the leopard in the mountains of the Cape Province. Management report, Cape Dept. of Nature & Environmental Conservation.

Norton, P.M. and S.R. Henley. 1987. Home range and movements of male leopards in the Cedarberg Wilderness Area, Cape Province. S. Afr. J. Wildl. Res., 17(2) : 41 - 48.

Norton, P.M. and A.B. Lawson. 1985. Radio tracking of leopards and caracal in the Stellenbosch area, Cape Province. S. Afr. J. Wildl. Res. 15(1) : 17 - 24.

Norton, P.M., A.B. Lawson, S.R. Henley and G. Avery. 1986. Prey of leopards in four mountainous areas of the south-western Cape Province. S. Afr. J. Wildl. Res. 16(2) : 47 - 52.

Pienaar, U. de V. 1969. Predator - prey relationships amongst the larger mammals of the Kruger National Park. Koedoe 12 : 108 - 76.

Schaller, G.B. 1972. *The Serengeti Lion.* Univ. of Chicago Press.

Seidensticker, J.C. 1977. Notes on early maternal behaviour of the leopard. Mammalia, 41(1) : 111 - 13.

Smith, R.M. 1977. Movement patterns and feeding behaviour of leopard in the Rhodes Matopos National Park, Rhodesia. Arnoldia, 13(8) : 1 - 16.

Stuart, C.T. 1986. The incidence of surplus killing by *Panthera pardus* and *Felis caracal* in the Cape Province, South Africa. Mammalia, 50(4) : 556 - 58.

Sunquist, M.E. 1983. Dispersal of three radiotagged leopards. J. of Mammalogy, 64(2) : 337 - 41.

Wilson, V.J. 1968. Weights of some mammals from eastern Zambia. Arnoldia, 3(32) : 1 - 20.

Wood, G. 1986. The Lazy Leopard. In Magnum magazine, Aug. 1986 p.40.

ABOVE Painted reed frog.

Data Collection and Validity

The Game Report Records were kept on a daily basis from before 1990, and submitted to the warden of the Sabi Sand at the end of the month. Except for particularly well-known animals, no attempt was made to identify individuals, prides or herds, and no consistency was maintained. Thus some records of, for instance, the Flockfield male survive from that period, but only when whoever was writing up the daily log mentioned him by name. Toward the end of 1989, William Taylor began to organise the records in a more consistent fashion, and from the beginning of 1990 I started identifying the various animals by assigning them a constant name and preparing a monthly analysis, showing their occurrence on a map of the area. Later I institutionalised this report as one of the duties of the senior ranger, so that a system of maintaining the records could be perpetuated. Sightings on Marthly, Eyrefield, Mala Mala and Flockfield are compiled by the senior ranger at Mala Mala camp, while Charleston and Toulon are covered by someone from Kirkman's or Harry's. In the south, Dieter Sovak kept accurate and detailed records from the beginning of 1989, so that much useful data from this time on was preserved for that part of the reserve. The daily log was intended to be as informative a record of available data as was possible under the conditions, with a strong emphasis on continuity. An especially enthusiastic recorder, for example, might sacrifice a great deal of his spare time in detailing the log and compiling the report, making of it a considerable undertaking that might not easily be shouldered by the next person to take it over. Such a situation could lead to delays in writing up material, and

ultimately loss of data. This is an important consideration in a private operation such as Mala Mala, which is very guest intensive and where the days are full. The daily log consists therefore of a simple entry of basic data: species, identity of individual or group, position, and what it killed, in the case of predators. A final column, less frequently used, records behavioural items; mating, interactions, etc. The data is thus of a very rudimentary nature, but it was surprising how much came out once I started to analyse it. Questions such as seasonality of mating and of births could be addressed. Chris Daphne took over the game report in 1994 and has managed to enter a wealth of subsidiary data since then and on a regular basis, making of the daily log a far more informative record than had previously been the case. I was able to use much of this to good effect for the period from June 1995 onwards, after I had left the area. Such instances as the fights and interactions between female leopards had been recorded in full. My greatest regret from the time I spent there is that I did not keep any form of personal journal. A quantity of useful information concerning animal behaviour was thereby lost, as well as the memories and thoughts of the time. The essential details of an interaction between the Mlowathi male and a female leopard were forgotten, for example, because I did not write them down immediately after the drive nor during the days that followed. I eventually acquired, though too late to be of any but the smallest amount of use, a small dictaphone which is ideal for this purpose. I recommend such a machine to any person in similar circumstances. Hopefully people will recognise interesting situations regarding leopards that they might see after having read this book, and record them more faithfully than did I.

Statistical Validity

Persons of an academic persuasion may be interested in the statistical biases inherent in this study. It would be difficult to assign any unit effort to the sampling. In general, the more vehicles that were out, the more animals were located. If all the camps were full, a total of sixteen vehicles would be operating. During quiet periods – such as before the election in 1993 – the number might be as low as one or two. However, there is no direct link between the number of vehicles out and the game that is likely to be found. The unit effort was not constant; a leopard with cubs, or with a kill, might be at a particular location for some days, and the viewing would be concentrated on that area with little effort made to find leopards elsewhere. Sometimes a number of vehicles will co-operate in looking for leopards, depending on what guests wish to see. At other times, a camp or all camps may be booked out by groups, which often organise activities such as bush cocktails or communal dinners. These involve all the camps meeting at a specific place, so that a fair amount of time is spent simply travelling to and from that spot with more time set aside for the particular activity. Consequently fewer animals tend to be located on such drives, although a lot of vehicles are out. For these reasons and other similar ones, a direct return per unit sampling excursion is difficult to assess. Perhaps no single completely reliable method of calculating a predator's diet exists. The presence of a vehicle is likely to influence the outcome of a hunt where direct observation is employed, as Schaller pointed out in 1972. The greatest amount of care is exercised so as not to interfere with a hunt, which involves maintaining the greatest distance from the participants as is possible and keeping lights off them at night. In strict scientific terms, however, an outside influence is present. A usual consequence of a vehicle's presence is to make a prey animal more alert and vigilant. Using kills that have been made, and that predators are feeding on tends to bias the sample in favour of larger prey. Smaller animals are likely to be promptly consumed and therefore not found as kills with a predator lying up nearby. Faecal analysis, if possible, can compensate for this by revealing the small animal component in a predator's diet. Absolute values are, however, difficult to obtain from this method owing to variable rates of digestibility of prey animals. It is also often impossible to ascertain whether an animal whose remains are reflected in a scat was killed or scavenged, and how much of it was consumed. The majority of kills recorded during this study were found as carcasses on which leopards were feeding. Some were recorded as kills made while leopards were being followed at night, and far fewer by day. Virtually all the small animals that were recorded were seen being caught, which is as would be expected considering how quickly they are eaten. In view of the amount of time that was spent following leopards, it is perhaps surprising that the number of prey items in this category is not larger. Scat analyses tend to show a fairly large number of small prey in a leopard's diet, although in terms of bulk they are possibly not a very significant food source. Using this method, Bailey found that small mammals ranked second in importance, on a percentage occurrence basis, to ungulates. They constituted only 4% of the kills that he found, but at least 29% of the scats that he examined contained their remains. One might expect, therefore, to see leopards catching a greater number of small animals than were recorded in this study. Here I believe that the effect of the vehicles is to be seen. Besides causing a small creature to bolt for cover or freeze, the noise may also prevent a leopard from hearing such prey. Statements such as

this may alarm people into thinking that the leopards were unduly harassed. It refers, however, to a strict scientific appraisal of the means of data collection. When following animals hunting, every effort was made to interfere as little as possible. Leopards were seldom seen actually catching their prey, since when they were stalking, lights were doused and engines killed. The antelopes were in general habituated to vehicles as well, although as potential prey they had a greater flight distance and were more inclined to be nervous than were the large predators, so it happened that we were often able to watch a hunt being conducted with neither of the participants paying any attention to their audience. Ranges, or territories, could not be estimated with an assurance of precision and for this reason I have not calculated or estimated their sizes. Some of the land, for example, was not covered at all by us excepting the very few occasions when animals were followed into it. The area east of the Chellahanga river is one such example. And given the patchy nature of our sightings of individual animals, a part of a range might be overlooked – especially if it happened to be in one of the abovementioned areas. However, over the length of time that some of the animals were seen, it is likely that most of their ranges were recorded. Range sizes have moreover been accurately estimated for different areas through radio telemetry. Where a study such as the one that forms the basis of this book is useful is in determining long-term issues such as land tenure, constancy of borders and interactions between individuals.

ABOVE The common sandpiper, a summer migrant invariably found in rocky streams.

ABOVE And so a new generation begins and the cycle of life continues.